MOTHER'S HOPE

A MIRACLE ON SKID ROW

By Kurt Salierno

with Esther Bailey

Mother's Hope: A Miracle On Skid Row

Copyright © 2006 by Kurt Salierno

ISBN 978-0-9786285-3-6

Other books by Kurt Salierno:

Living On Skid Row, Stories of Kurt's start in ministry on skid row

Mercy Beyond Measure, Bible Study work for *Living On Skid Row*
By Kurt Salierno and Barry Shafer

Saddle Soar, Inspirational stories of Kurt's bicycle ride across America

Still Living On Skid Row, More great true stories of Kurt on the streets

Additional copies of these books are available by mail or web site.
www.KurtSalierno.com

Kurt Salierno
P.O. Box 1868
Kennesaw, Georgia 30156

Cover by Don Wright, WrightDesigns, donwrightdesign@comcast.net

Cover Picture, used by permission

Printed in the United States by Morris Publishing
3212 East Highway 30
Kearney, NE 68847
1-800-650-7888

Dedication

I dedicate this book to my mom, Evelyn Laird, my mother-in-law
(I prefer to call her mother-in-love) Rena Marvel, and my stepmom,
Mary Salierno. All of them have taught me how precious a mother's
love is. Each, in her own way, has been an important part of my life
and more precious than words can express. My life is enriched by their
influence and I am blessed beyond words because of each of them.

About the Author
Pastor Kurt Salierno

Kurt Salierno has been a pastor to the homeless for more than 30 years, most recently in Atlanta, Georgia. He is the founder of Church On The Street, a ministry to the homeless across the country. Salierno is an author, speaker, and avid fisherman. Salierno's other books are *Living on Skid Row*, *Mercy Beyond Measure*, and *Saddle Soar*.

For more information, visit www.KurtSalierno.com.

About the Coauthor
Esther Bailey

With more than 1,000 published credits, Esther Bailey is also author of *Pass the Perks, Please! and God's Little Messengers*. She and her late husband, Ray, have been family friends of Kurt and Lori Salierno for twenty years. Living in Scottsdale, Arizona, Esther attends McDowell Mountain Community Church.

"Esther's work on this project has been immeasurable as she helped put my thoughts into words. She is highly gifted in making sense of my scribbles, understanding my thought process and making a book come together."   Kurt Salierno.

Table of Contents

Introduction

After serving as pastor of Church On The Street for seven years in Atlanta, Georgia, I asked God for a fresh idea. "Lord, show me a unique way to create a spiritual hunger in people whose lives have hit bottom," I prayed. As an afterthought, I added, "If it's all the same to You, God, I'd just as soon have an idea that won't get me shot at or dragged into the police station to explain my presence in a place where trouble breaks out." In the many years of street ministry, those were all realities.

As I waited for God's answer, my thoughts turned to the upcoming holiday - Mother's Day. The woman who carries a child within her own body for nine months, and then nurtures that child through the stages of life, maintains a powerful influence that carries even into adulthood.

In the United States, Hallmark tells us that 96% of American consumers participate in Mother's Day, on some level. It has historically been the busiest day for long-distance telephone calls, the busiest day for florists, the busiest day for restaurants, and second only to Christmas in gift-giving. People in many ancient cultures celebrated holidays honoring motherhood, documented as far back as the early

Greeks and Romans. Mother's Day is a special day!

In the South, like no other place in the country, a mother is considered to be the key figure in the family - even more so than the father who is absent in many homes. If the homeless and the addicts connected with their mothers on this special day, perhaps tender memories of the past would spark an interest in getting help to turn their lives around. I have seen it happen many times. If nothing else, I thought, it would be good to reconnect loved ones for prayer and support.

As the thought grew stronger, I felt compelled to offer my cell phone free of charge to anyone who wanted to reconnect with Mom on her special day. This was in a time that cell phone companies charged its customers by the minute. The idea of unlimited calling was not heard of as yet - especially long-distance calls. If disturbed by the possibility of running up a phone bill beyond my budget, I simply relied on a cliché that had proved true for me in times past as well as for many before me. When God calls someone into action, God provides the necessary tools to accomplish the task.

I began my involvement in street ministry in Portland, Oregon where I attended Warner Pacific College. When I was involved in local church ministry during the last 25 years, I have always connected with the homeless in the area we served. Some would say it was a calling. I just call it, "following the heart and mind of Jesus who dwelt among us." For the past several years, I have served exclusively as pastor to the homeless. I am following my heart and passion to live on the streets as I did during my college years.

The name Skid Row is a place recorded first in Seattle, Washington, where logs were skidded into the water on dirt roads for delivery to lumber mills. During the great depression, the area went into decline, and "skid row" became synonymous with "bad neighborhood." All of the larger cities in the country have an official or non-official Skid Row. My ministry has been focused on Skid Row of various towns in the United States. In most areas called Skid Row you will find the majority of homeless people.

My wife has a high-profile ministry that requires her to travel extensively. With considerable effort fine tuning our schedules, we are able to combine ministry and family life. For several nights a week I sleep with the men in a shelter or under a bridge. By being with them, I can minister to them more effectively. As their "pastor," I want to be accessible to help them change their lives.

Every night, somewhere in the inner city, we hold a worship service with singing, preaching, testimony and food. Volunteers help prepare meals to feed and organize clean up after the crowds leave. We call that Church On The Street. Much of my ministry, though, takes place one on one. When someone comes up with a need, my volunteers and I do our best to meet it. The need may be for a job, clothing, a medical emergency, or protection from harm. Sometimes I'm attacked by an enemy or required to break up a fight, and I have a collection of knives and guns intended to do me in. The weapons remind me of God's providence.

Along with providing tangible assistance, we are constantly on the lookout for an opportunity to point people to the healing power of Jesus Christ. Answered prayer quickly gets the attention of those involved in the situation. One day I huddled together with others under a bridge to stay out of the rain when a man needing employment approached me. A short while after our prayer on the spot, a man driving a truck came along asking, "Does anyone need a job?" Such incidents serve as faith builders to the community and to me.

Now I had another idea to put to work. On the Saturday before Mother's Day, I parked my truck in the worst part of Atlanta and put up my cardboard sign outlined with florescent colors that read: "Call your mother for Mother's Day–FREE." Sitting in one of the two chairs, I waited. Not more than ten minutes later the first homeless man approached me and wanted to call his mother. I invited him to sit down while I dialed the number. On the phone I said, "This is Pastor Kurt with Church On The Street. Your son is sitting beside me and wants to say hi for Mother's Day." I handed the phone to him and listened to the brokenness in his voice as he took the first step toward home. My heart broke as I watched a flicker of hope mixed with sadness in his eyes when he said, "I love you."

By the time he finished the conversation, several people had lined up. One man approached me with the question, "Is this a joke?"

"No, it's for real," I said. "If you want to call your mother, stand in line, and you will be connected when it's your turn." The line was already two blocks long.

A large assembly of people on the streets that belong to the homeless population makes the police nervous because trouble often breaks out. Although the people in line were calm and orderly, a policeman stopped to ask what was going on. When I pointed to the sign, he smiled, nodded approval, and went on his way.

To make sure the cell phone wouldn't die, I kept it charged with a battery charger from my truck. All day Saturday and after church Sunday the phone held up. Some people stood in line as long as four hours to make the call. During those two days my emotions ranged between heartbreak and hope – heartbreak because I observed the human condition at its worst. Hope because I know how Jesus Christ can change lives.

True conversions on the streets are rare, but then they aren't exactly prevalent in the general population either. In Christ's own words, "Small is the gate and narrow the road that leads to life, and only a few find it" (Matthew 7:14, NIV). In spite of limited returns, the value of one soul makes ministry on the street worthwhile. When someone in the ghetto experiences God in a life-changing event, the result is nothing short of miraculous.

Each person in the ghetto has a different story. Life before the streets. The downward spiral. Utter despair. I've heard the stories over and over–different stories with a common ending.

Mother's Day weekend allowed me to look into the depths of human souls. Their private struggles to cope with life gone wrong are forever etched on my heart. In addition to what I learned to be true, I permitted my imagination to fill in the blank spaces. To me, several of the Mother's Day experiences continue to read like a novel in my mind.

My purpose in sharing these stories is to show what happens when an idea inspired by God is brought to fruition. I know many people were touched and blessed. With each blessing bestowed on someone else, my heart was doubly blessed.

Each time my mind recalls the essence of a story, I find myself praying for the individuals involved. As precious people who have lost their way are introduced to you, will you please take time to cover them with your prayers? Perhaps you may look at a homeless person with different eyes. One of a mother who has lost her son or daughter. Believe with me that Jesus is still in the business of changing lives!

Chapter 1

David

Whishhh! If David hadn't leaned to the left, the stone would have hit him in the head. In a moment another rock hit the target and David reeled with pain. It was only a matter of time before the boys in the gang sent him to the hospital – or worse. All David knew to do was run. He had been running all of his life and could he ever run. Some day he hoped to run far away from Alabama, far away from everyone he knew.

The bullies were losing ground, but David could still hear their insults and threats. "Dummy, Dummy, Dummy!" they shouted. "We'll get you, Dummy!" They often did, and David had the scars for proof.

Not this time, David said to himself as he rounded the corner to a gas station. For a few seconds he was out of sight from the gang. He quickly chose his hiding place and crouched down behind a pile of tires. He held his breath and waited until the boys ran on by. With his energy spent, he could not face turning around and going back home. The gang would just be after him tomorrow and the next day and the next ...

Just then a truck loaded with Christmas trees pulled up to a gas pump. Two men got out and both headed inside. One of the men stopped at the counter to prepay for the gas and the other one went to the restroom. Only one other car was on the lot and the driver was about to pull away. What if? ...Could he? ... Adrenaline began to race through his veins as he considered the possibility of undertaking a new kind of adventure.

On sudden impulse, David walked to the back of the truck. Looking around to see no one in sight, he crawled into the truck and hid his body among the Christmas trees. The pine needles scratched his skin and it was hard to breathe in the confined space. David's heart began to race and he wondered if he had made a terrible mistake. Would life on the run be even worse than life at home?

For only a few seconds David considered jumping out of the truck and heading home. When the two men returned to the truck, that option closed. "Man, it's cold here," one of the men said as he dipped the squeegee into a solution and cleaned the windshield. When the other man brought the hose back to the gas tank, David was only a few feet away. He feared the beating of his heart might make his presence known. Fortunately, the sloshing of the gas into the tank muffled the sound.

The man pumping gas said, "Yeah, it's cold here, but cheer up. We should be in Florida day after tomorrow. Then we'll head back home with money for Christmas presents."

Realizing he would not spend Christmas with his parents this year caused a strange emotion to stir in David's heart. On one hand, he would miss spending the time with his parents. He loved them and he knew they loved him. They always found a way to give their only child a nice but inexpensive present, but they always apologized because they wanted to give him so much more. That made David sad because he knew how hard they worked to provide for him.

By Christmas this year, his parents would realize that David would not be home. Dad would not have to work long hours at the factory to make up for time off without pay during the week of Christmas. Mom would not have to decorate the house and bake cookies after a late shift at the cleaners. Mom and Dad will be better off without me, he thought.

Realization that he might never again see his parents brought tears to David's eyes. How he would miss Mom's hugs and Dad's kind words! There was no one else to show him love. But even they did not understand how much it hurt to take the abuse from the kids at school or in the neighborhood. The older David got, the harder it was to deal with his learning disabilities.

In a terrible moment years ago, David learned that he was different from other children. Something was very wrong with his brain. Mom and Dad had taken David to the doctor. After examining David, the doctor asked the nine-year-old to join Aunt Katherine in the waiting room. By sitting close to the door, David was able to hear the conversation.

"I'm sorry to give you bad news," the doctor had said. "David's brain has not developed normally. His mental capacity will always be years behind that of other children his age. He will always be slow."

"Will he catch up?" Mom asked.

David had listened intently, but all was silent on the other side of the door. Finally, the doctor cleared his throat and spoke. "No. In fact, he will likely fall farther behind as he gets older."

Even at an early age, Mom's sobbing brought sorrow to David's heart. He knew he was the source of her pain and there was nothing he could do about it.

"What should we do?" Dad had asked.

"There are places where ..." The doctor cleared his throat again. "There are places where children with mental disabilities can be cared for by people who understand their condition."

"No! No!" Mom said emphatically. "My child won't be raised in an institution. We'll care for him ourselves."

"In that case, you'll just have to take each day as it comes. I'm really sorry," the doctor had said.

Much of the conversation was above David's level of comprehension, but he fully understood that he was different and that he was a problem to his parents.

From David's first year in school, the other kids ignored him; so David kept to himself. With no friends, he felt very much alone and out of place. At the beginning of every school year, the teasing started, especially when David had to repeat a grade.

At age twenty, David was the oldest student in the senior class.

It was his second year as a senior, but David did not expect to graduate. His parents kept him in school because they didn't know what else to do with him.

"I don't want to go to school any more," he had often told his parents. "The teacher knows I'm dumb and the kids pick on me."

Mom always bowed her head and closed her eyes tight. David thought she did that to keep from crying. Dad had to keep David appraised of their decision. "I'm sorry, David, but your mother and I have discussed all the options. We believe it's better for you to remain in school for a while longer."

"How much longer?" David always asked.

"At this point we can't say but we want you to know that we're putting your interests above everything else." David believed that his parents thought they were doing the best for him but they didn't understand the pain that he endured each day.

It seemed that memory of all the major events of David's life were compressed into the first few moments of his new adventure. From now on, that life would be a mere memory as he went on to ... to what? Where would he sleep? How would he eat? What could he do with his time? Those were scary questions without answers but they also promised a bit of excitement. Whatever the future held, it would be better than the past.

The pine needles continued to prick David's skin. When he touched a sore spot on his forehead, blood oozed onto his fingers. With no handkerchief or Kleenex on hand, he pulled the back of his shirttail around in front to wipe his fingers. Under his jacket, the stain wouldn't show.

The truck had been moving slowly with frequent stops through city traffic. As soon as their speed increased on the expressway, the wind picked up and David shivered in the cold. He tried to put more trees closer to him to block the wind but his strength was no match for the heavy trees. The best he could do to try to keep warm was to curl up into a little ball, close his eyes, and hope to sleep. Unable to put his mind to rest, David began to muse about a recurring dream he had at home. In the dream, David was running far, far away. Now he was living that dream.

David knew that it would soon be dark. He needed to get out of the truck but, first, he had to make plans. When would the time be right? Had he gone far enough away from home so that the bullies could not find him? They had driven several hours. Surely he would now be safe.

Of course he worried about what would happen if the truck drivers caught him. They might call the police and he would end up in jail. That was an experience he hoped to avoid forever. With that possibility of trouble with the law in mind, he needed to make his exit with the utmost caution.

A few miles later, the truck exited the highway and pulled into a gas station. Was this the time to make his break? With an increasing need to go to the restroom, David decided to take his chances. Still, he wanted to be cautious. He edged his way out of the branches of the pine trees. Then he would be ready to jump as soon as the truck stopped. Maybe he could make his getaway before the men got out of the truck. If they saw him, he would run. With so much practice in running, he was sure he could outrun them with no problem. Excitement ... or was it fear? In any event, his pulse raced and his body trembled as he prepared to make a fast exit.

David's feet hit the pavement even before the driver turned off the ignition. In the restroom, he locked the door and struggled to catch his breath. One look in the mirror, as well as a stinging sensation on his face, told him the pine needles had not been kind to him as he disturbed the branches. He wet a paper towel and wiped his face. The sap from the trees was not easily removed but he rubbed until his skin turned red.

When someone tried the door, David's heart began to race again. The men would both want a turn in the restroom before they traveled on. If they hadn't seen him, of course, they would think he was just another traveler from one of the other cars. The thought somewhat relieved his fears but, nevertheless, he wanted to take no chances. As soon as he could no longer hear footsteps, he quickly left the restroom and hid behind the dumpster in back of the gas station.

In response to the growl of his stomach, David opened the dumpster to look for food. Nothing but a bunch of empty boxes and paper. The hard facts of life "on his own" began to sink in. If he could find no food, how could he survive?

After the truck loaded with Christmas trees pulled away,

David walked a short distance to a restaurant. Surely he could find food in the trash can there. Everything was wrapped in plastic bags. David opened one of the bags but the odor of the mess inside turned his stomach. Searching through several other bags brought him nothing but a stale roll. This part of his adventure was not to his liking.

Now what? David wondered. Aimlessly, he started to walk. Where to? He had no idea. He didn't even know where he was except that he was far from home. That had been his goal for a long time. One thing for sure, he was in a busier place than he had ever been before. He had to dodge many cars as he made his way through traffic.

The events of the day had brought weariness to David's body. It would be great if he could just sit down and rest but there were no benches along the streets as there had been in his hometown. Even if there had been a place to sit down, though, it would be too cold to relax. Maybe everyone was moving so fast to keep warm. There were people all around him, but they went on their way and paid no attention to David. That was the way he liked it.

Actually, most of the people he saw were very much like David. They looked like they had been having a hard life too. Their clothes were dirty and worn. Perhaps many of them had learning disabilities too. At last David might find a place where he could fit in - a place where no one would abuse him or make fun of him.

If he had wanted peace and quiet, though, David had come to the wrong place. The roar of traffic, the sound of automobile horns, police and ambulance sirens pierced the air. David decided he would get used to the noise and the bustle of activity would keep him from getting bored. He would grow to appreciate his new lifestyle.

As darkness descended, David wondered where he would find a place to sleep for the night and how would he fill his empty stomach? How much of a price would he have to pay for his freedom? Whatever, David decided; freedom would be worth the price.

Everyone seemed to be in a hurry. Several men in a group seemed to know where they were going and David began to keep pace with them. He stayed a short distance behind because he didn't want to intrude on their space. Long ago he had learned the hard way that it was safer to stay out of the way of others.

When the men turned the corner, David followed. One of the men turned around to face him. Oh boy, here comes trouble, David thought.

"Are you going to the meeting?" the man asked.

"Uh ...uh," David stammered with fear. The friendly face, although dirty and unshaven, put him somewhat at ease. "Yeah, sure," he said. Might as well find out what it's all about, he thought. After all, he was on an adventure.

"I haven't seen you around before."

"I just got here." To David's relief, the stranger merely nodded without further comment. It would be hard to explain what he was doing when he didn't even know where he was.

When they turned another corner, David's mouth flew open and his eyes grew wide as he witnessed the scene ahead. A parking lot was set up with chairs all in rows like a school room. Unpleasant memories flooded his mind. Should he run while he could? he wondered. Even as the thought entered his mind, he dismissed it. The last thing he wanted to do was make a scene.

A pleasant looking man with sparkling eyes extended his hand to David. "Welcome to Church On The Street. I'm Don," he said.

The word welcome eased David's anxiety. "Thank you," he said.

So this is a church? Now he noticed the trailer up front with the sign painted on the side. At first he couldn't make out the words but it took him only a short time to figure them out: Church On The Street. Church had never been part of David's life. There were a few churches in the small town in Alabama, but David had never attended one. He always wondered what church was all about. Now he was about to find out.

People kept coming until nearly all the seats were filled. A man stood up front, asked everyone to stand, bowed his head, and began talking to God as though God was listening. These people's minds are worse off than mine, he thought. Looking around at the crowd, he was surprised to find that everyone's head was bowed. People's lips were moving as though they were joining in with the leader. Actually, the strange behavior made David feel at home. He should fit right in here.

After the man said, "Amen," everyone sat down.

A woman stepped forward and announced they would sing.

Not everyone sang the words together, but some people certainly seemed happy. Sometimes they stood while singing and sometimes they remained seated. David followed along with what everyone else did.

After they sang for a long time, Don got up and said he would read from the Bible. David didn't know anything about the Bible either, but he listened as Don read, "God so loved the world that he gave his one and only Son, that whoever believes in him should not perish but have eternal life" (John 3:16, NIV).

Only two words stood out in David's mind: God loved. He didn't understand the rest of the words but he knew about love, although he never experienced it except from Mom and Dad. No one else loved him. At best they put up with him; at worst they abused him. David knew God only as the Big Guy in the sky.

"Put your name in the verse instead of the world," Don said. "God loved John, God loved Jessica, God loved Andrew ... or Paul ... or Jim." He paused to allow the concept to sink in. "How does it feel to know that God loves you?"

Awesome! David thought. That was a word he learned from school. Especially to the younger kids, anything that seemed the least bit unusual was awesome. With that definition, though, the concept that God loved him needed a stronger word. But David didn't know of a stronger word; so awesome would have to do.

Don kept on talking ... and talking ... and talking. It would have been hard for David to sit still so long if he hadn't kept hearing over and over again that God loved him. Maybe God's love could take over in his life where his parents' love left off.

When Don finished, he came back to again shake David's hand. "Hi, what is your name?"

"David," he replied as he shook Don's hand.

"You'll stay and eat with us, won't you, David?"

The eating part got David's full approval. A grin spread across his face as he said, "Yeah. Man, I'm hungry."

"All right! You came to the right place."

A quizzical expression crossed David's face. "Where am I?"

Don placed his hand on David's shoulder. "You're at Church On The Street."

"I know that, but I don't know where we are."

"Do you know you're in Atlanta?"

"No.... Is Atlanta in Alabama?"

"No, Atlanta is in Georgia."

David had never heard of Atlanta or Georgia. "Is Georgia a different country?"

"No, Georgia is a state right next to Alabama."

"I see." It felt good to ask questions and not be told how dumb he was. David had the feeling he was going to like it here.

People were lined up and going behind the trailer. They received a plate filled with two hot dogs and a big bowl of chili and beans. David could hardly wait to get his hands on a plate like that. So many people were ahead of him that David began to worry they might run out of food before he had his turn. Anxiety continued to build until he got close to the trailer and saw mounds of food - enough to feed twice this crowd.

With his plate full, David sat down in a seat near the front to enjoy his meal. He was so hungry he stuffed nearly half a hotdog in his mouth at once. After that, he took smaller bites because he wanted to make the delicious taste last as long as possible.

David had finished eating and was wondering what would happen next when a woman came up to him with a nice looking jacket. "It looks like you need a warmer winter jacket," she said as she extended the jacket to David. "See if this fits."

With his eyes dancing, David started to try the jacket on over the one he wore but he couldn't get his left arm in the sleeve. He kept trying to maneuver his arm through the sleeve.

"I think it will work better if you take off the other one," the woman said with a smile.

The jacket was a perfect fit for his large body. David handed his old jacket back to the lady.

"You may keep both jackets," she said. "You'll need the light one when it's warmer." When David awkwardly fidgeted with the jacket, the woman said, "Let me get you a backpack where you can keep your personal things." She went into the trailer and returned with a brand new back pack, which she handed to David.

"Thank you," he said. Wow! I'm not going to miss Christmas after all, David thought. This is better than I would get at home.

With no where else to go, David hung around until nearly everyone else had gone. He still had a problem–a big problem. Where was he going to sleep?

Don asked the question that was on David's mind. "Where are you staying tonight?"

"I don't know."

"You don't have a place to stay?"

Hanging his head, David said, "No." He felt ashamed that he was unable to take care of himself.

"That's okay. We're here to help." David could tell that Don really cared about him. He cared about everyone.

"There's a homeless shelter not far from here. You can stay there," Don said. He called to another man and asked him to take David to the shelter.

As David started to leave with the other man, Don said, "We'll look forward to seeing you again – maybe next week."

Apparently the church didn't feed people every day in that parking lot. On the way to the shelter, David learned from his companion that Church On The Street had a church service and provided a meal to the homeless somewhere in the city every night. You would just have to learn the different places where they serve and when. This was the regular spot for Thursday night.

"In time you'll learn the ways of the street. I'll show you what I can." As they walked, David's new friend pointed out a restaurant where they could often find some decent food in the trash can. In a mall they could hang out and keep warm as long as they kept moving. His adventure would continue as he learned how to survive, David decided.

Even as tired as he was, David had trouble going to sleep at the shelter with so many bodies lying close to him. Would someone hurt him during the night while he was asleep? Would someone steal his new jacket? Many thoughts disturbed him until he finally drifted off into troubled sleep.

In his dream David was home. Mom was standing by the door crying, "Where is he? Where is he?" Over and over she repeated the agonizing cry.

Dad stood by her side and tried to comfort her. "He'll be back." he whispered. "He'll be back." Mom buried her face on Dad's shoulder and continued to sob.

David opened his mouth to speak but no words came out. He wanted to go to Mom and tell her he was okay, but he couldn't move. It was as though he was trapped in an invisible body. Then he began to float through the air until he woke up sobbing.

"Hey, cut it," the guy in the next bed yelled.

When fully awake, David muffled his sobs and said, "Sorry. Bad dream." The rest of the night he hovered between sleep and consciousness. At times he longed for a hug from Mom but his arms remained empty. He was glad when morning came.

A cup of hot coffee was a good start for the day, but one of Mom's warm cinnamon rolls sure would taste good. Every time his stomach called for food, David reminded himself that he had had a good meal last night. Many of the men were already leaving as though they had some place to go. David hoped that someone would invite him to go along, but no one did.

When he could no longer remain in the shelter without becoming conspicuous, David strapped on his backpack and walked aimlessly outside. In the brisk air, though, he quickened his steps and headed for the restaurant where he might find food. A piece of toast and an overripe banana was all he could find. He ate the toast, wrapped the banana in a napkin he pulled from the trash, and placed it in his backpack for later.

At the mall he walked around the buildings twice before he could get inside. Besides getting warm, David enjoyed window shopping. He stopped at a jewelry store to look at a watch that reminded him of the one Dad gave Mom for her sixtieth birthday. He wished he could buy her some earrings that he knew she would like.

Thoughts of Mom brought back his dream. He could not bear the realization that Mom and Dad would be worried about him. Somehow he had to let them know he was okay, but how? He couldn't write a letter and he didn't have a telephone.

In one of the shops, a lady placed her cell phone on the counter when a friend called her aside to look at some jeans. The two women were busy examining the jeans and no one else was around. David was sure he could snatch the phone without being caught. Stealing was a terrible thing to do but David was desperate. He opened his backpack so he could hide the phone quickly and stepped into the store to stand before the counter. With no one watching, he grabbed the phone and made a fast retreat.

For several moments David's heart raced and his body trembled. As he walked, his mind was in turmoil. Although grateful that he had not been caught, guilt stabbed at his inner being. He had hurt someone else the way he had been hurt. That wasn't right. That was not right at all. At the same time that guilt overwhelmed him, David had another concern. While he remained in the mall, he feared he might yet be caught. If he sat down on a bench to make a call, the woman might come by and recognize her phone.

In spite of hating the thought of leaving the warmth of the mall, David knew he had to get out of there. Outside, he had nothing in mind except to get away to some place safe to make his call. When the lady who owned the phone discovered it was missing, she would probably call to have the service turned off. That's what Mom did when her cell phone was once stolen. He wanted to make the call before the service was turned off.

He ran out to the busy street and found a hallway in between two tall buildings where he decided it would be safe to call. He pushed the numbers that he had learned when he was a little boy. His parents had him repeat the number until it was etched on his mind. While waiting for Mom or Dad to answer, he rehearsed what he would say. Instead of hearing Mom's voice, he heard a woman say, "I'm sorry your call cannot be completed as dialed. You must first dial the area code and then the number." What did all that mean? David wondered. Had he stolen a phone and hurt someone else for nothing? He didn't know what an "area code" was. He did not need to do that before in his hometown.

When David found himself in front of an appliance store, he noticed a big screen television in the window. One of the programs he often watched at home was on. He began to get interested and laughed at the funny parts. The man inside noticed him and opened the door to come outside. David started to move on.

"No, don't leave. Would you like to come inside and watch TV?" the kind man said.

"For real? You mean it?"

"Yes, you look cold and tired."

"Yeah, I am. Thank you," David said as he followed the man inside. It was good to sit down and get warm.

Just when hunger pangs began to take over David's thoughts, his benefactor said, "I brought a sandwich for lunch today. I'm not that hungry. Would you like to share it with me?"

"If it's okay, I'd really like that."

They went in the back room to eat. "A bell will ring if a customer comes in," the storekeeper explained.

After devouring the bigger half of the chicken salad sandwich, David took a big gulp of soda and started in on the potato chips. When he finished eating, David wondered what to do about the telephone call. If he was going to get through to his parents, he would have to have help because he did not know anything about codes the woman mentioned.

"Is there anything else I could do for you?" the man asked.

This was probably the best opportunity he would ever have. David plunged right in to explain his problem with the phone. "She said something about codes."

"Oh, yes. Area codes. Tell me where your parents live."

After locating the area code, the kind man explained the extra numbers David needed to use to call his home. Then he handed the ringing phone to David.

Would anyone answer? he wondered. When Mom answered after four rings, David was so nervous he could hardly speak. "Mom," was all he could say.

"David, where are you? Are you all right? Will you be home tonight?" Her questions all ran together.

"I just want to let you know I'm okay, Mom. I love you."

"I love you too, David, but your father and I are worried about you. Let us come and get you."

"No, Mom, I'm okay, but I needed to get away. I couldn't stand getting hurt by the boys anymore."

"Just come home, please, David, and we'll figure something out."

"No, Mom. I can't. I gotta go." David hung up the phone before Mom could say anything more.

Tears were near the surface but, if he was going to break down, David wanted to be alone. He managed to say, "Thanks for your help," before rushing out the door back into the cold.

Time began to drag. David tired of trudging the streets but he couldn't think of anything else to do. When he saw a pay telephone on the corner, he felt a ray of hope. At home he had learned to check the coin return box for change. No luck this time, but someone had left an empty soda can on the shelf. Aluminum cans could be returned for cash; so David placed it in his backpack.

Although he knew that Church On The Street would not return to that location until next week, he began to walk in that direction anyway. When he reached the site, he found a concrete block where he sat down to think. Talking with Mom had caused homesickness, but he wouldn't even consider returning home. All he asked of life was food to eat, a place to sleep, and – most of all – peace from his tormentors. Somehow, just being in the parking lot, where the church had treated him so well, brought him a good feeling.

It was here that David learned that God loved him. "Would God still love him after he stole the phone?" he wondered. Mom certainly did not love whoever stole her phone. She talked about that terrible person for a long time.

Overcome by feelings of guilt, David had to get rid of the cell phone. He wished he could return it to the owner, but that was impossible. Removing the phone from his backpack, he tossed it in a pile of weeds. The act did not relieve the guilt at all. If the owner did not have the service turned off, someone might find the phone and run up a big bill – maybe even make a call to China. To prevent anything like that from happening, David retrieved the phone and smashed it into a hundred pieces.

He then ate the banana that would have to suffice for his evening meal.

When the shelter opened for the night, David had been waiting outside for a long time. In fact, he was the first to arrive. As other men joined him, they shared more tips for surviving on the streets. "Always check out parking lots for money. When people take car keys out of their pockets, they often pull out change that falls to the ground," someone explained. He learned where to take aluminum cans for cash and what places he should avoid. Treading on a gang's territory could put him in the kind of danger he had run from.

Surprising to David, the two-block area where Church On The Street just met was one of the most dangerous places in the city. "It's called the pit of hell," he was told. Just last week someone was murdered there. It was the practice of Church On The Street to set up in the most dangerous areas of the city.

"Why do they do it that way?" David asked.

"They want to take the story of Jesus to places where it's most needed," someone explained.

David shuddered. With the news, a dark cloud like an ominous threat seemed to envelop David's being. Apparently he had a lot to learn about survival on the streets. One of the first things he wanted to do was find all the locations of Church On The Street. It was there he felt safe.

Chapter 2

Billy

Although he had had enough sleep, Billy did not want to get up and face the world. With nothing to look forward to, it was less painful to pull the sheet over his face and block out the midday sun. At eight o'clock tonight he would begin his shift at the all-night diner. Until then he had time on his hands.

The worst part of Billy's mundane existence was realization that he alone was to blame for his lot in life. Not too many years ago he would have spent free time hiking a nature trail or hanging out with friends.

Friends could be a blessing or a curse. Choosing the wrong friends landed him on skid row. Why, oh why had he gone along with Jack's suggestions? The question was never far from his mind.

It all started at the gun target range. "Hey, man, you're good," Jack said after Billy hit the second bull's eye. Billy liked the recognition.

Later, Jack said, "You need to turn your talent into cash."

With interest mounting, Billy asked, "How?" It would be good to find something better to do than pumping gas.

"When an opportunity comes up, I'll let you know." Jack's answer left Billy with a sense of anticipation mixed with curiosity. Maybe he could play a bit part in a movie. The man with the quick draw. Although he doubted if he actually had a movie career ahead of him, his mind began to imagine the different scenes he might play.

Every few days Billy asked Jack, "How can I make my gun pay off?" His friend always put him off.

Just when Billy was about to run out of patience, Jack said, "Well, Billy, are you ready to 'bang bang' for a buck?"

"Yeah–more than ready," Billy said with a wide grin on his face.

As Jack described step by step plans for the heist, adrenaline surged through Billy's veins. Several times Billy tried to interrupt, but Jack just talked louder. "Now, do you understand what you are to do?" he asked after he described Billy's role a second time.

"Uh ... uh ... I didn't expect to get involved in ... in armed robbery."

Jack laughed. "It seems kind of scary the first time but you'll get used to it. Think what you can do with all that bread!" The money tempted Billy. While still under the influence of Jack's spell, he agreed to go along with the deal. In the years since, how often had he remembered that moment and shuddered?

When time came up for Billy's trial, Jack had skipped the country to a place where the law had been unable to find him. Had Jack planned from the beginning to escape and leave Billy to take the rap if trouble came? Billy often wondered. Caught in the act, Billy could only plead guilty. The Public Defender merely asked for lenience because it was Billy's first brush with the law, and on the films, he played no part in the robbery. He just stood there almost in a daze of disbelief that this was happening.

Mom and Dad were in the courtroom on the day Billy was sentenced, but their presence brought him no comfort. He was too ashamed to face them. Even after nearly four years, he could still see the pain in their eyes as he was led away to begin serving his sentence.

Even now, out of jail, every time he saw his parents' eyes in his reverie of the past, Billy had to turn his mind elsewhere. Throwing the sheet off his face, he got up, brushed his teeth, splashed cold water on his face and dressed for the day. In addition to cereal and milk for his midday meal, Billy opened a can of peaches and ate them all. Fortunately, he was able to take his evening meals before his shift began at Majestic Diner. When he finished eating, he nursed a second cup of coffee while taking a reality check of his future.

In the eight months since his early release from prison, Billy had accumulated seven hundred dollars. At that rate, he should have two thousand dollars in no time. With that amount of money, he would head back home to make a fresh start. He hoped to turn the look of pain in his parents' eyes to a look of joy - even pride. He did not want to risk becoming a burden to his parents who did not have extra money to throw around. Until he could stand on his own two feet, he would continue to work at Majestic Diner.

Jobs for ex-cons were hard to come by. Ex-con – how Billy hated the label even though he realized it was well deserved. Actually, he was not sure he could claim the ex status. For eleven more months he was still on probation. He had to keep regular contact with his probation officer to check his progress. The probation officer was helpful and encouraging. It was through him that he landed his position at Majestic Diner. Each week he had to show proof of employment documented with check stubs. Any travel plans beyond his apartment and work had to be cleared with the probation officer. He thought of his probation period as his second sentence.

The restrictions did not bother Billy except for the implication that he could not yet be trusted to take his place in society. From the beginning of his prison term, he had decided to make his life right. More than anything else he wanted to go home, tell Mom and Dad he was sorry for bringing disgrace to the family. He would then work and make an honest living to prove that he was a good citizen.

During his prison term Billy had had no contact with his family. He never questioned why they did not come to visit him. He understood that was how his family was. They really never talked about "trouble" in their lives. It would have been too hard to face them anyway until he had redeemed himself. Incarcerated more than two hundred miles from home, he would not have wanted his parents to spend time and money on a visit to him. With Dad's disability, Mom was the only one who worked to pay the bills. Thinking about his parents now, Billy wondered if they even knew he had been released from prison.

As he put the milk back into the refrigerator, his mind lingered on the note he had posted on the outside. "Clean up my life and go home." The reminder was also on the bathroom mirror and in his empty wallet. Nothing would deter him from that goal.

After finishing with the dishes, he still had nearly four hours to kill before it was time to leave for the diner. With nothing else to do, he decided to walk to the diner instead of taking the bus. Since he had no friends, time spent at work became his social life as well as his livelihood. With no television at home, his entertainment consisted mostly of dreaming about a better future when he earned enough money to return home.

Last night was unusually busy at the diner. He lost track of how much he had earned in tips, but a few people were extra generous. Tips had to be turned over to his boss named Clem, but they were then included in his paycheck. If business was good today, maybe the boss would ask him to start an hour or so earlier to earn a little extra. Maybe he would even have an opportunity to work the grill. During the time he had been employed, he had worked himself up from dishwasher to busboy to waiter. Most people wouldn't consider that to be a big deal, but to Billy it was a miracle.

Actually, Billy liked the restaurant business. Making good on his own began to build his self-esteem that had reached bottom after the burglary. His job brought him so much satisfaction that he considered building his life's work around the food industry. When he left home, there was no shortage of restaurants and new ones were probably springing up all the time. By the time he returned home, maybe he would be in line to take a job as a chef. Someday he might even own his own restaurant.

Chapter 3

Erica

During her teenage years, Erica often felt trapped by the confines of family and a small town. After graduating from high school, she headed south for the freedom of city life in Atlanta. With her family only three hours away, she figured she could keep in touch with home when she felt the need.

To cut down on expenses, Erica lived in an apartment with a roommate. Even so, her job at the pizza parlor barely covered her rent and car expenses. What good was her freedom if she had no money to spend? Resorting to plastic money, she began to go into debt. Bills soon piled up. Life was not at all like what she had intended.

One day the cook at the pizza parlor said, "Hey, Erica, I'm having a party at my house Saturday night. Want to come?"

"Yeah. Sure," Erica said as her spirits perked up. That was what she needed – a party. Life in the city began to look up. She had made the right choice after all.

When the restaurant closed on Saturday night, Erica went home to change clothes. Along with her slinky black pants, she chose the low-cut lace top she had purchased in hopes of finding such an occasion to wear it. Looking in the mirror, Erica teased her black hair and applied bright red lipstick. Smiling at her reflection, she vowed to forget her money worries and concentrate on having a good time.

Besides the other workers from the restaurant, several people who came to the party were strangers to Erica. With two glasses of beer in his hands, a man who looked to be in his fifties sauntered up to Erica. "How about a beer for the belle of the ball?" he asked as he handed the drink to Erica.

The girl accepted the drink with mixed emotions. It was good to take a drink but she did not welcome the attention of the stranger. When she finished the beer, he said, "Another beer for the belle of the ball?"

She liked the phrase, the belle of the ball. "Yes. Thank you," she said.

After a few more beers, the man suggested, "Why don't we go up to my place for some real fun?"

Erica knew what he meant. She was not looking for sex - at least not with this man. Lowering her eyes, she vigorously shook her head.

"I'll make it worth your while," he said.

The words sobered her for a moment. Could this be a way to assuage her money worries? She looked at him with questions in her eyes.

"A hundred bucks," he said.

Wow! That would help ease the financial crunch.

"I need another beer," she said. She had another ... and another. And then she left the party with the stranger.

The following day Erica did not wake up until after noon. The stench of stale beer nauseated her and her head ached, but that was nothing compared to the feeling of self-loathing. She jumped into the shower but water could not wash away the filth. Would she ever be able to live with herself again? she wondered.

At work on Monday morning the cook taunted her about what had happened.

"I'm sorry," she said. "It won't happen again."

"Don't apologize. You made my friend happy. He wanted to know if you would be available in the future too."

Erica merely shrugged her shoulders. She did not want to discuss the matter.

Just before the restaurant closed, the cook found Erica alone. Pinning her against the wall, he said, "How about a favor for a friend?" His lascivious grin turned her stomach. She tried to push him away, but he waved a hundred-dollar-bill in her face. The temptation to work out of the bondage of debt was greater than her loathing for what she was about to do.

Plunging quickly into the downward spiral, Erica soon gained the reputation of being "available" if the price was right. When her extra activities interfered with her job, she was fired. No matter, though. She made enough money on what she thought of as her "new job."

Drugs, of course, came with her occupation. Heroin and crack allowed her to escape reality. When her roommate threw her out because of clients who visited at all hours of the day and night, Erica found a room she could afford in a rundown building in a bad section of the city. Because drugs had first claim on her money, she often had to move from place to place.

For a while Erica had tried to maintain contact with her family without revealing the details of her personal life. When her parents pressed her for information, conversations turned ugly. Taking the easy way out, Erica had stopped calling.

Chapter 4

Marlene

In spite of being raised in a motel setting by a single mother, Marlene had a happy childhood. Mom managed Mountain Breeze Motel in south Georgia near the Florida border. Just off of the freeway, the motel was a hot spot for truckers. Some of the regular guests called the motel their home away from home. Mom worked hard to keep the place clean and inviting.

"Traveling is hard work," Mom often said. "People are tired when they get here and they need a comfortable place to relax." Marlene couldn't believe that traveling was hard work. She longed for the opportunity to go places and do things she only heard others describe. In all the years when she lived in the little apartment connected to the motel, Marlene had never had a vacation.

Not that she ever complained. They were fortunate to have a nice place to live as part of Mom's employment package. Besides, motel living was a good deal for Marlene too – especially after Mom convinced the owner to turn the vacant lot into a playground for the children.

Many families stopped at Mountain Breeze Motel on the way

to Florida's entertainment center. When Mom wrote up the reservations in the guest book, she wrote the names and ages of the children in red ink. It was Marlene's job to greet the children and entertain them. Every day she checked to see if any children would be coming. On days when the weather was bad, she played games with the children in the lobby. Like most of the children, though, Marlene preferred spending time on the playground.

Of all her childhood memories, Marlene cherished her time spent with Leonard the most. His family stopped at the motel on the way to and from Disney World every year. As they sat on the swings, Leonard would tell Marlene all about the rides and fun things to do there. The two seemed to bond instantly although Leonard was a couple of years older than Marlene.

One year as soon as Leonard left for Disney World, Marlene began to look forward to his return. As she checked the reservation register one day, she realized that Leonard would be back on her birthday. She asked Mom to bake some cupcakes for the occasion.

"I'll be glad to do that," Mom said. Just as she took good care of her guests, Mom did her best to make a good life for her only daughter. Marlene had always been proud of her mother.

On the day that Leonard was to return, Marlene waited eagerly for his arrival. As soon as the station wagon pulled in, Marlene met her friend with two cupcakes topped with thick chocolate frosting and a candle. "Today's my birthday," she said.

"How about that? Mine was last Thursday. I wish I had known

about your birthday. I would have bought you a present when I was in Florida. Anyway, thanks for the treat and happy birthday!" he said as he accepted the cupcake.

Seeing Disney World through Leonard's eyes thrilled Marlene. Sharing magic moments with her friend nearly took her breath away. "I wish I could have been there with you," she said.

"Yeah, I do too." He paused and then added, "It was great but it wasn't as much fun as being here with you."

Leonard seemed like the brother Marlene always wanted, but all too soon he was gone. "I'll be back next year," he promised.

After he left, Marlene wrote to Leonard in Kentucky a few times, but he never wrote back. She had formed friendships and even became pen pals with other children, but her heart longed to hear from Leonard. Would he really come back next summer? she wondered. Or had he forgotten her? Maybe she hadn't meant as much to him as he had meant to her.

One day, when Marlene had almost forgotten about Leonard, Mom finished a telephone call and said, "Marlene, guess what?"

"I can't guess. Tell me."

"I just got a reservation from Leonard's family."

All the excitement came rushing back. Only three days until his arrival but it seemed like three weeks or three months.

As soon as the family arrived, Leonard and Marlene headed for the playground. They sat in the swings and talked about everything that had gone on in their lives since they last saw each other. In

Leonard, Marlene had found her soul mate – the brother she had always wanted.

All too soon, they had to say good night because Leonard's parents were ready for bed. "I'll get up early to see you again before you leave," Marlene said.

Shaking his head, Leonard explained. "We'll leave at five o'clock in the morning. Dad wants to drive through the city before the streets get crowded."

It was a long time before Marlene was able to go to sleep that night. When she got up the following morning, Leonard was gone. She began to look forward to his return. Each evening, she marked off one more day on the calendar.

When Leonard returned from Florida, he handed Marlene a little package. With a twinkle in his eye and a grin on his face, he said, "Happy birthday!"

Marlene gasped. "You remembered. Thank you, thank you, thank you," she said as she jumped up and down.

"I hope you like it."

Tearing off the paper, Marlene again gasped at the sight of the red tee shirt with a Florida beach scene printed on the front. "I love it. It's perfect. Thank you."

"Since you can't get to the beach, I brought the beach to you."

Before the two headed for the swings, Marlene changed into her new tee shirt. "I'll think of you every time I wear it," she said. "And I intend to wear it a lot."

When Leonard left, Marlene treasured the tee shirt even more. It was hard to believe that such a cute boy would choose her as a special friend. Now she had something tangible to remind her of their time together. The only time Marlene took off the tee shirt was when Mom said it had to be washed. She even wore it when Leonard returned the following year, although it was a bit tight. That year he brought her a little vase made of sea shells.

Each year Leonard brought her a birthday present to add to her collection she kept in a box she called her "treasure chest." She often thought that she would grab that box first if a fire ever broke out in the motel.

As the years passed, Leonard meant more to her than a brother – much more. She wasn't sure when she first fell in love with him. Perhaps her diary held the secret but she no longer had the little book where she recorded her youthful fantasies. She remembered referring to him as her Prince Charming.

For Leonard's return from Florida, Mom had baked a birthday cake for her to share the special occasion with her boyfriend. Leonard had lighted the fourteen candles and said, "Make a wish and blow them out."

She didn't share her wish with him, but her dancing eyes probably said that she wished she could marry Leonard and live happily ever after.

When they finished the party, they went to the swings in their favorite place under the oak tree. It did not occur to Marlene to wonder why Leonard had not given her a birthday present as he had in previous years. She just enjoyed being with him and hearing about his experience on water skis. When he told her about his fall, she said, "I wish I could have been there to see that."

"Don't be so happy about it. I could have been injured for life."

"But you weren't. And I'm glad you weren't hurt." Marlene could think of nothing that would have been worse than for Leonard to be in pain.

Several times Leonard started to say something and then just gave her a mischievous grin. What was he up to? she wondered. Finally, he stopped swinging and pulled a little package from one of the cargo pockets on his jeans. "I got you something special this year," he said but did not hand her the package.

She studied his face and decided he was stalling to make the moment last. "What is it?" she prompted, but he still did not respond. Her curiosity was mounting. "What did you bring me?"

When Leonard finally handed her the package, she did not open it at first. It was now her turn to prolong the moment.

"Aren't you going to open it?" Leonard asked a bit impatiently.

"Not yet. I'm trying to guess what it could be. What makes it special?"

"Give me the package," he said.

"No," she teased. "You gave it to me and I'm not giving it

44

back."

"I'm not fooling. I want the package," he said in a stern tone.

Somewhat startled, Marlene asked, "Why?"

"I want to put it on you."

Handing over the package, Marlene anticipated his touch. Whatever it was, he would most likely have to touch her to put it on her.

When Leonard started to open the box with a jeweler's name imprinted on the lid, Marlene stared in awe. "Oh!" she gasped as she fixed her eyes on the necklace with a golden cross accented with Leonard's and her birth stone. Were the rubies real? she wondered. No matter, though. Nothing could have been more precious to her.

"This is the most beautiful thing I have ever seen," she said.

"It's no more beautiful than you are." On impulse, Marlene threw her arms around Leonard and kissed him on the lips. He kissed her back, much harder than before. Surprised by the intensity of her emotion, she backed away. As Leonard placed the necklace around her neck, she felt a tingling sensation throughout her body.

"There," Leonard said. "It looks good on you." He squeezed both of her hands. "Wear it always and it will bring you luck."

"I'll wear it forever. Thank you. Thank you."

Her necklace became Marlene's most valuable possession. The cross was offset to one side and had a slight twist on each of the two intersecting pieces. Every compliment she received about the beautiful cross brought tender thoughts of Leonard.

The following year Leonard did not return to the motel. She received a letter from him telling her that his mother had started a new career. Vacation time for her did not coincide with his father's time off; so they probably wouldn't be making any more trips to Florida. For two weeks, Marlene slept with the letter under her pillow and cried herself to sleep.

Marlene's life had gone downhill fast after losing Leonard. There were plenty of teens to hang out with but she never again developed the kind of close relationship she had with Leonard. It was during her time of grieving about Leonard that she found temporary relief from her pain by sniffing cocaine and smoking pot. Soon the desire to get high consumed her thinking and she needed more and more drugs to keep going.

Her already mediocre school achievement record dipped lower and lower. It was touch and go as to whether she would graduate, but she did receive her diploma – just barely. After graduation, her only ambition was to find enough money to support her drug addiction. Oh, just to be a child again and swing on the playground with Leonard, she often thought.

Soon after Marlene's graduation, a dozen college men checked into the motel on their way back from the beach. "How many rooms will you need?" Mom had asked when one of the guys stepped up to the registration desk.

"We probably need several but we want only one." In response to Mom's incredulous expression, he added, "Gotta save money somewhere."

"I'll give you some extra supplies but I can't provide twelve of everything for one room."

"That's okay. We'll share."

"And I'll expect the room to be in good shape when you leave."

"Yeah. Okay."

After the men went to their room, Mom brought out four towels, two bars of soap, and two blankets. Shaking her head in wonder, Mom said, "Marlene, will you take these to our latest guests?"

"Sure, Mom." Marlene was glad for an opportunity to spend a few moments with the bunch of cool guys.

"Stay and talk to us," someone said as Marlene started to go after delivering the supplies.

"I'd like to, but I have to get back. We have several reservations coming in." She smiled and then added, "Maybe later."

"Is that a promise? We'll party most of the night."

"Yeah. As soon as Mom closes for the night, I'll be here." A tingling sensation spread throughout Marlene's body. She hadn't been this excited since Leonard gave her the necklace. Even without a fix she was plenty high because she knew refreshments would be served at the party. Maybe she would have a chance to experiment with something new. She was ready for a night of adventure.

All of the guys took an interest in Marlene and made her feel special. While holding Marlene in his arms, one guy said, "I have yet to find a girl who is as much fun as you. Why don't you go back to Atlanta with us?" The other men also began to urge her to accept the invitation.

"That sounds exciting and I'd love to, but I wouldn't even have a place to stay."

"We'll hide you in the dorm rooms until you can find a place of your own."

Marlene hesitated only a moment. This was her opportunity for the excitement of life in the city. There was nothing for her if she stuck around the motel. "I'll do it," she said.

"Why don't you go pack your bags now? Bring them back here and we'll grab a few winks of sleep before we head off in the morning before anyone else is awake."

The arrangement sounded perfect to Marlene. After packing her bags, she sat down to write Mom a note. She hated to disappoint Mom who had done so much for her, but she had to do what was best for her. "The guys invited me to go with them to Atlanta, and I hope you will understand that I need a change. Don't worry about me. I'll be all right. Thanks for all you've done for me. You're a good mother." She was about to place the note on the kitchen counter but Mom might get up in the night for a drink of water and spoil her plan. Instead, she took the note with her to place on the motel desk before she left.

Everything was packed in the three cars that would leave for Atlanta. Which car would she ride in? Marlene wondered. None of the guys was in good shape for driving, but Marlene did not think of that then. The two near-accidents that happened on the way were only the beginning of living life in the danger zone.

In Atlanta, the guys shuffled Marlene from room to room. They seemed to get annoyed every time she asked for drugs. After only a week, the man who had first extended the invitation to come to Atlanta said, "Marlene, it's not working. We like to party too, but we can't keep up with your addiction. You'll have to leave right away."

"Where will I go?"

"That's your problem."

Sobered by the ultimatum given in such an uncaring way, she thought of an idea. "Maybe I could let the college know you brought me here."

The guy scratched his head. "Yes, I suppose you could do that. Ok. You can stay for a few more days. In the meantime, I'll see if I can work out something."

Two days later, a man named Fred came to the dorm to meet Marlene. After they had a couple of drinks together, Fred said, "In exchange for sexual favors, I'll give you a place to stay and keep you in drugs."

The offer was made in a matter-of-fact business manner with no tenderness whatsoever. That wasn't really the kind of relationship Marlene wanted, but what other options did she have? "All right," she said. To herself, she added, only for a little while.

When she called home, Marlene found it hard to tell Mom that everything was going well for her. "I'm living in a nice apartment with a roommate," she said. If Mom had asked the roommate's name, Marlene was prepared to say, "Freda." In her mind, that was at least close to the truth.

At Fred's suggestion that she find a job, Marlene went to work as a cocktail waitress and soon moved on to become a waitress and dancer in a nude club. By merely telling her mother she was a waitress, she could maintain the illusion of respectability. She didn't like the person she had become but she wanted to spare her mother the heartache of knowing that her daughter had violated every facet of decency.

After a few months of living with Fred, Marlene became pregnant. When her condition became apparent, her image didn't fit the bar scene. Fred continued to take care of her through the pregnancy, but he warned her that she would have to leave when the baby arrived. "I'm not into being a family man," he explained.

The first few months of life on her own with a baby were hard. Because Fred had supplied her with enough drugs to keep her satisfied, she had saved some money from her earnings, but that would run out soon. What would she do then?

The man who had supplied her drugs since the breakup with Fred seemed to be attracted to Marlene. By using all the seductive powers she had learned on the street, maybe she could make an arrangement with him. It took little more than a week for her wiles to work. Not only did Bernie ask her to move in with him, he welcomed little Brittany as well.

While living with Bernie, Marlene had a second child she named Ashley. She had a man and two children in her life but she certainly wasn't living the American dream. During a heavy drug party one night, everyone passed out. Some time after midnight, Marlene woke up to see her children asleep in the middle of the floor. It wasn't a pretty picture. Drug users were sprawled everywhere, the odor of liquor mixed with smoke permeated the air, and a hard-core pornographic film blared from the television. How did she get from the playground to this? she wondered. The worst part was she didn't know how to get out.

But one thing she knew for sure. She had to get her children out of that kind of environment. Quickly she went into action. First, she stole all the cash she could find from the others who were passed out and then she packed up the children's clothes and caught a taxi to the bus station.

At the bus station, Marlene learned that she would have to wait more than an hour before a bus would head for her hometown. Little Ashley was still asleep but Brittany woke up and asked, "Where are we, Mommy?"

"We're at a bus station, Sweetheart. We're going to ride a bus to your grandma's house."

"I don't know Grandma."

"I know. I'm sorry you don't know her, but you'll like her. I promise." Thinking about what she was going to do wrenched Marlene's heart but there was no other way. Her children deserved better than she could give them.

All the while they waited, Marlene battled fear. What if Bernie woke up and guessed what she was up to. He hadn't abused her but she had never crossed him before. If he realized she had stolen money from him and his friends, no telling what he might do.

Finally, she was safely on the bus with her girls. Breathing a sigh of relief, she leaned back in the seat, hoping to sleep. It would be another four hours before the girls could start a new life. And she?... She would not think about what the future might hold for her.

The girls were awake by the time they reached their destination. In the taxi, they asked many questions. Often Marlene pointed out places of interest she remembered from her early years. Finally, Mountain Breeze Motel came into view.

When they reached the playground, Marlene asked the taxi driver to wait while she gave full attention to her girls. It was going to be hard to pull off her plan when her heart was breaking. The girls' enthusiasm at the sight of the swings, though, made it easier. "This is where Mommy played when she was a little girl," she explained. "You'll love it here and Grandma will love you and take good care of you."

Before Brittany could ask a question, Marlene headed back to the taxi. "Could I use your cell phone?" she asked the driver.

When Mom answered, Marlene began to pour out the story she had never told her mother. "My life's a mess and I have two children – little girls, Brittany and Ashley. I love them but I can't take care of them. I need you to love them and take care of them like you did for me. They're on the playground and I have to go. I'm sorry – so sorry."

"Marlene, wait. Please come home."

"I can't, Mom. My life's too messed up. Go to the girls, now!" With that, she hung up the phone.

Marlene asked the driver to move away where she could watch the children without being seen. Mom stooped down to pick up Ashley and took Brittany by the hand. As soon as they went into the motel, Marlene had the driver take her back to the bus station.

For hours, Marlene had been operating on nervous energy. On the bus headed back to Atlanta, she needed a fix and needed it now. She had been deprived of drugs for more than twenty-four hours and she was about to "crash," but it would be four more hours before she could hope to satisfy her craving. In a panic, her breathing became labored. She put her head on her hands in an effort to control the tremors.

A man seated across the aisle two rows back tapped her on the shoulder. "Do you need help?" he asked.

All Marlene could do was stare at him with her eyes glazing over.

"I have some meth," he said softly. He took the nod of Marlene's head and her smile as an invitation. He sat down beside her and allowed her to share his stash of crystal meth.

As the drug began to take effect, Marlene relaxed. A sense of peace replaced the troubling emotions she had battled all day. "Thank you," she said to the stranger who continued to sit beside her. "You saved my life."

"I'm glad I could help."

It felt good to be traveling back to Atlanta with someone who understood her situation. She would need to find someone else to hook up with. Maybe he could give her some leads. For sure, she wanted to stay clear of Bernie. After stealing his money and walking out on him, she knew he would not think kindly toward her.

Life back in Atlanta did not go well at all. Desperate for drug money, she ended up on the streets as a prostitute. Dancing in strip clubs was her only other source of income. Most managers of strip clubs allowed women to dance nude in the clubs for half of the tips they received. At first, the lifestyle was distasteful and she wanted out. In time, though, she accepted the degenerate lifestyle as the best she could do.

Marlene phoned her mother and talked to her children occasionally, but she never let emotion get out of hand. When Mom begged her to come home, Marlene quickly changed the subject. It was easier to manipulate the conversation when she was stoned.

While on the streets, Marlene learned about Pastor Kurt, who was always ready to help in an emergency. At first, she felt uncomfortable around a man of God, but Pastor Kurt offered hope and comfort instead of condemnation. He often said, "God loves you and has a plan for your life if you will invite Jesus into your heart." The message sounded good, but Marlene could not quite believe it would work for her.

Chapter 5

Leonard

Sitting on a bench outside the church, Leonard waited. Surely the church service would be over soon. Finally, people began to file out the door. Leonard began his game of sizing up the people to determine who would be the best target. Church was a good place to pick up cash, but if he miscalculated and picked the wrong person, he might end up with nothing.

The pastor stood at the door and greeted everyone in a friendly manner. "Thank you for coming, Mr. Brown. I hope you're feeling better." "We need to get together for a game of golf this week." He had a smile and a word of encouragement for everyone. It was apparent that the pastor genuinely liked people. Leonard decided to make his pitch to him.

"Hello, Pastor. I'm sorry I couldn't make it in time for church."

"We would have been delighted to have you, but maybe you can make it next week."

"No, I'm just traveling through, but I never miss church if I can help it. I'm on my way to a new job in Birmingham, Alabama, but

I ran out of gas a mile or so down the road. I decided to walk to church and figure out what to do after that."

"I'll take you to your car and we can pick up a can of gas on the way."

That was not the response Leonard wanted. "Oh, no, I wouldn't want to put you out. I need the walk to keep up my exercise anyway. But I could use a few dollars for gas if you can spare it. Some unexpected expenses along the way took all of my cash and I haven't had a chance to get to an ATM machine."

The pastor pulled out his billfold. It definitely was not bulging with cash, but the pastor handed him a ten-dollar-bill. "Will this help?"

"Yeah. Sure." Disappointed, Leonard started to walk away. Remembering his manners, he turned and said, "Thank you."

Ten dollars was more than he had before but it wouldn't go very far on the drug scene.

After wandering aimlessly for a while, Leonard decided to take a rest in a nearby park. As he came upon a little restaurant, he automatically stopped to check the trash can. Dark bread. He especially liked dark bread. It looked like a customer hadn't touched the bread because there were several slices all together. Today seemed to be his day. He found enough lunch meat to put together to make a sandwich, which he placed in the plastic bag he carried in his backback.

At the park, Leonard sat on a bench to watch the antics of a squirrel for a few minutes. When the squirrel scampered away, he pulled out his sandwich from his backpack. He was about to unwrap it when a man came along walking a golden retriever. When the dog began to move toward Leonard, the man gently pulled on his leash and said, "No, Dodger."

"Dodger's a nice boy," Leonard said. "Could I give him a bite of the sandwich?"

"No, we never feed him from the table."

Leonard put the sandwich away and motioned for Dodger to come closer. The man released his leash. As Leonard began to pet the dog, Dodger became very friendly, putting his feet on the bench and licking Leonard's hand. To the man, Leonard said, "If you're not in a hurry, maybe you could sit and visit for a while. I need someone to talk to."

"Yeah. Dodger and I can use a break." Sitting beside Leonard, the man asked, "So, how's everything with you?"

"Well, it's not the best time in my life. My wife's in the hospital and the bills are piling up. I just came out here to think. There must be some way I can get through this, but I sure don't know how."

"Are you working?"

"Yeah. Six days a week in construction but, even with overtime, I fall farther behind every week."

"Do you have insurance?"

"Yeah, but many of my wife's needs aren't covered."

"That's tough. I'm really sorry."

"I don't suppose you happen to know of an agency or anyone

that offers assistance for extreme hardship cases."

"No, I'm sorry I don't, but ..."

When the man hesitated, Leonard knew it was time to step up the sad story. "I really don't care about myself but it breaks my heart to see my kids suffer. I couldn't even buy my little girl a pair of shoes."

The man reached into his pocket and pulled out a twenty-dollar bill from his billfold. Handing the money to Leonard, he said, "This should be enough to buy your daughter some shoes."

"Thank you. Thank you. I'll tell her all about you and Dodger and she'll thank you every time she looks at her new shoes."

"I'm glad I could help."

Leonard could hardly wait until the man and the dog moved on; so he could do some serious business on the street. He decided to eat his sandwich on the way because he didn't want to waste any time before he could get his next fix.

The drug business was not like other businesses. Dealers had to keep a step ahead of the law. To avoid arrest, they often changed their places of operation. Leonard knew of a crack house in the ghetto that was usually open, but that was some distance away, and he needed a fix now. Walking down a familiar alley, Leonard ran into Ziggy, with whom he had previously done business. "How's business today, Ziggy?" Leonard asked.

"Great. Just great."

Leonard knew that dealers often indicated a booming business to discourage customers from expecting a better deal, but he was wise to the ploy. Holding the twenty-dollar-bill in his hand, he asked, "What's the best you can do for me for twenty?"

Ziggy held up his smallest bag of crack. "Come on, Ziggy. You can do better than that." When Ziggy shook his head, Leonard started to put the money into his pocket. "All right. I guess I'd better take my business elsewhere.."

As Leonard started to walk away, Ziggy said, "No. No. Let's deal."

With a grin on his face, he began to bargain with Ziggy. "How about two bags?"

"Two bags for thirty dollars."

"Can't do."

Holding up a larger bag, Ziggy said, "Twenty dollars." Leonard knew it was a good deal, but decided to hold out just a little longer. Actually, he liked playing the game.

When Leonard walked away with the two bags, he once again prided himself on his people skills. That was how he survived life on the streets. Now to find a safe place to smoke crack and then he would move on to the crack house where he could get the best deal to beef up his supply. He could deal with not knowing where his next meal was coming from, but wondering how to get his next fix filled him with anxiety. Only his drugs gave him a sense of peace.

It had been five years since Leonard had contacted his parents. His use of drugs began while he was in high school. When his parents found evidence of drug use in his room, a big fight followed. The pressure became so intense that he knew he had to find a way out. He had to go some place where he could find peace. The city. He had already tasted city life and liked it.

During spring break of his sophomore year, Leonard had heard several of the seniors talking about going to Atlanta. With his friendly smile and way with people, Leonard was invited to go along. That was a trip of a lifetime. Drugs. Girls. Experiences he had only dreamed about. He was hooked.

Realizing he didn't have enough credits to graduate anyway, Leonard left home during his senior year of high school. Atlanta was great for a while but, without a high school diploma, he couldn't find a job that suited him. Soon, he lost his ambitions and settled for making it just one day at a time. When he was young, people used to say that someday he would make it big. "If anyone in our small town is going to go places, it will be Leonard," some of his parents' friends often said.

Thoughts of earlier days constantly filled Leonard with a sense of failure. He had really blown it and he didn't know how to get back on track. At those times, drugs were the only antidote to ease the pain.

Chapter 6

David - Saturday before Mother's Day

After four years on the street, David had encountered the best and the worst of human behavior. The kindness of a few people made it possible to survive. Their generosity always warmed his heart. More people were out to rob him or beat him up, but David tried to stay clear of them. Still, he had been robbed or beaten up more times than he wanted to remember. One time he ended up in the hospital after a severe beating.

Most people simply looked the other way when they saw a homeless person. That irritated some people but being ignored was okay with David. He didn't want to be a bother to anyone else.

On this particular Saturday, David headed for Woodruff Park, where he sometimes found people willing to share their food. The pretty spring day was perfect for a walk, and David enjoyed the singing of the birds as he traveled along. He was about to turn a corner to avoid a dangerous area when he noticed a long line of people on the sidewalk leading to an unusual sight. Pastor Kurt was sitting on a chair in front of his truck. What was going on? David wondered. The chairs weren't set up like normal when Pastor Kurt had Church On The

Street, but people were lined up waiting for something to happen.

Torn between curiosity and hunger, David decided to see what was happening at the church. Maybe they were giving out free food or something. When he got closer he saw a sign taped on Pastor Kurt's truck. He struggled to read it as big words were impossible for David to read, but he could usually figure out the small ones. In time, that is. He stared at the brightly colored sign that read: "Call your mother for Mother's Day–FREE."

Wow! That was good news. It had been a while since David called home. So he walked back to get in line for his turn to call. Sometimes he had enough change to call from a pay phone but, more often, he stole a cell phone. After all those years, he still felt guilty every time he stole a phone. It was easy to find one in the tourist area of town. People often left purses and phones in their cars. Too easy, David thought. He called only often enough to keep his parents from worrying. Also, he hated for his parents to press him to tell them where he was.

With several people in line it would probably be some time before David's turn, but he decided to wait. The opportunity might be gone by the time he got back from the park.

Pastor Kurt sat in one chair and the person making the call sat in the other chair. Pastor Kurt always wiped the phone clean and dialed the number before handing the phone to the caller. Some people looked happy after the call but others seemed to be sad. After only a few seconds on the phone, one woman left with tears in her eyes. Did her mother refuse to talk to her? David wondered. He was glad his parents still cared enough about him to want him to come home even though he thought it was better for them if he stayed on the street.

Many times in the past four years David considered returning home. He would try to find Pastor Kurt and see if he could arrange it. Twice, David remembers, he found the pastor and lost his nerve before asking the pastor to call. By now he felt ashamed of himself for being gone so long. What he did was not right, he thought. Even when Pastor Kurt offered to help him go home, David could never muster the courage to make it happen - even though he wanted to.

During the next call, David was close enough to hear what the man said. After telling his mother he loved her, he began to cry. "Mom, I'm so sorry for being an embarrassment to you. I want to change. I really do." When the man left in tears, David felt sad. He hoped his call would not turn emotional. He knew he was an embarrassment to his family too.

The longer David waited the more eager he became to talk to his parents. It would be so good to make the call for Mom's special day without having to steal a cell phone. Finally, he was next up. "Hello, David," Pastor Kurt said.

"Hi, Pastor Kurt. Can I call my mom?" David said as he reached for the phone.

"You sure can. Give me the number and I'll dial it for you."

Impatient, David worried that his parents might not be home. On the next ring, someone answered. "This is Pastor Kurt of Church

On The Street. David is here to wish you happy Mother's Day." David again reached for the phone, but Pastor Kurt held up his hand and shook his head. Why the delay? David wondered. Pastor Kurt began to stammer, "Uh ... uh ... I'm not sure I - I - I - I" A moment of silence as Pastor Kurt listened. "I'll see what I can do. Here's David."

Grabbing the phone, David said, "Happy Mother's Day, Mom," when he heard her voice.

"Thanks, David. It is a happy Mother's Day because you called. It's been a long time since we heard from you."

"Yeah, I know. I'm sorry."

"Don't you ever get homesick, David? Do you want to see us as much as we want to see you?"

The conversation had to end soon or David would be in tears. "I'd love to see you, but ... I gotta go. Someone else is waiting to call home."

When Pastor Kurt took the phone from him, he said, "David, can you stick around a moment until I get a break? I want to ask you for a favor."

"Okay." David wanted to get to the park in hopes of finding something to eat. If he could do a favor for Pastor Kurt, though, he wanted to help the man who had been so kind to him. Once, when David received the worst beating of his life, Pastor Kurt found him lying on the pavement and took care of him. David had been knocked out so that he didn't know what had happened until he woke up in the hospital with Pastor Kurt by his side. When he was ready to leave the hospital, he discovered that his boots and the little change he had were stolen. Pastor Kurt promised to find him another pair of boots, which he did.

Two of the calls that Pastor Kurt made didn't go through. It wasn't until a woman began a conversation that the pastor gave David his attention. "David, have you ever washed a car?"

What an odd question coming from the pastor. David didn't even know how to answer. "Well ... I used to help my dad wash his car."

"Good. My truck is awful dirty and I don't have time to wash it." The woman finished her conversation and the pastor turned to help the next caller. As David waited, he wondered what his friend had in mind. He liked Pastor Kurt. He heard Pastor Kurt often stutter when he talked and he knew how it felt to be "different" like David often felt. It was like they had a kindred spirit.

David thought to himself how safe he felt with Pastor Kurt and his friends at Church On The Street. He knew they never made him feel stupid.

After handing the phone to the caller, Pastor Kurt pointed to his truck. "See how dirty it is. I'm ashamed of it. With tomorrow being Mother's Day, I'd like for it to be clean. Perfectly clean!" Another caller interrupted the conversation but David continued to wait.

"Would you come back tomorrow and wash my truck?" The request seemed to be quite urgent.

"Yeah, I guess I could do that."

"Good. If you come back around lunch time tomorrow, you'll receive a big reward for washing my truck."

A big reward caught David's attention. How much money would he get for a big reward? he wondered. Sometimes he saw signs about a reward that was offered for doing something important. The amounts were different but they were always for more money than he had ever had. "Sure," he said. "I'll be here by lunch time." Besides, he thought, Pastor Kurt had always treated him well.

"Are you sure you'll be back? It's very imp-p-p-portant."

"I'll be here for sure," David said as he reached out to shake Pastor Kurt's hand.

"All right. Don't forget. I'll be ready for you."

On his way to the park, thoughts jumped around in David's head like crickets. Memory of hearing Mom's voice brought him a moment of joy but then he felt bad because he always disappointed her by cutting the conversation short. Excitement surged through him when he thought about the money he would receive tomorrow – probably more money than he could imagine. In between those thoughts, he hoped to find food to fill the empty space in his stomach and wondered why it was so important that he wash Pastor Kurt's truck. Why was he willing to pay a lot of money when he could go to a car wash much cheaper?

Not many people were in the park today. He knew if he waited, small groups of people often showed up on Saturdays to pass out food. He didn't think it was an organized thing, because no one came at the same time every week and sometimes no one came at all.

To his delight, a van pulled up with two cars following behind it. A number of the homeless in the park gathered around the van to see what the benefactors had to give away. David joined right in hoping for a good meal. He was hungry. Although the memory of just talking to his mother was fresh in his mind, hunger pains in his stomach gained all of David's attention.

Indeed the people brought food. Lots of it. It took them a little while to set up the table and bring out the containers of food. David liked to help when he could. When he helped, he sometimes received more food. That's not really why he did it, but it was a nice benefit. Today was no exception. This was a special day, David felt. Not only did he get to talk to his mom, he was loaded up with food to take with him.

For the rest of the day, David ate all he could from the bounty he was given at the park. It felt good to be full. He knew he had to empty his pockets of the remaining food even if he had to give it away. Rats that frequented the streets would come into someone's jacket looking for food as the homeless slept. He had seen it too many times to want to experience it himself. So, before David got to the shelter that night, he ate what he could, and gave the rest away to the homeless he knew.

In the shelter that night David went to bed feeling more

satisfied than usual. He had a good day and would have an even better day tomorrow. Even as he counted his blessings, though, he felt emptiness and longed for a hug from Mom.

Chapter 7

Billy - Saturday before Mother's Day

It was good to get outside in the sunshine even though a heavy haze hung over the horizon. For a change, the neighborhood was quiet except for a sinister threat of trouble that could erupt at any moment. Gangs, drugs, and prostitution were common even in day time. When the probation officer said, "Billy, are you staying out of trouble?" it almost seemed like a joke. Trouble was all around him but Billy was determined to stay clean.

Soon after moving to the ghetto, Billy learned which streets to avoid in order to escape potential violence. On the way to the bus stop each day, he went out of his way to avoid a two-block area that was often described as the "pit of hell." At the diner he sometimes saw headlines about a murder that happened in that area. Prostitution raids, drug rings, and street fights were too prevalent to report.

On this day, though, something different was happening in the pit of hell. From a distance Billy could see a crowd of people that extended for blocks. Unlike usual gatherings, this one was calm and orderly. A bright sign on the back window of a truck attracted his attention. He was too far away to read what it said, but curiosity

70

compelled him to walk toward the truck. In the most dangerous area around his neighborhood, he suddenly felt safe. Strangely, fear was replaced by a sense of anticipation. Whatever was keeping such a large crowd in check might have benefit for him too.

As he neared the green truck, the words of the sign were clear: "Call your mother for Mother's Day–FREE." The approaching holiday had not dawned on him before. For him, Mother's Day was cause for sadness rather than celebration. All he could do was look forward to the day when he would be worthy to take his place as his parents' son. Before that could happen, he still had to put his life back together.

The sight puzzled Billy. It's odd, he thought, that homeless people, drug addicts, and prostitutes would stand in line to call their mothers. What could they say to Mom? Why would they want to bare their shame to their mothers? Didn't they know the call would break her heart?

It was as though the scene was a magnet that drew him closer. A man in a clerical collar sat in a chair in front of the line. He dialed the telephone and then handed it to the person seated beside him.

When Billy came within earshot, he stopped to listen to the one-sided conversations. Tears punctuated the halting words – words like "I'm sorry" and "I love you." The next man to sit down addressed the other man as Pastor Kurt.

It seemed that Pastor Kurt shared the emotions of the callers. Tears welled up in his eyes and sometimes streamed down his face. Some people had little to say but others talked for a long time. When the phone conversation was over, Pastor Kurt patted each person on the shoulder, and said encouraging words such as, "God bless you," or "God loves you."

A sudden urge to call his mother startled Billy. It wasn't time yet. He needed more answers. How long would it take him to earn enough money to start over? How long would he have to report regularly to the probation officer? When might his probation period be suspended? Billy didn't want to take shadows of his past into the future reconciliation with his family.

In spite of all his misgivings, Billy found himself in line to make the call. From the way the line moved, he estimated it would take a couple of hours to wait his turn. He had plenty of time to kill. There was very little conversation among the people in line. Perhaps they, too, were rehearsing their lines for an important drama in which they would soon star.

The smile on the face of a man who had just finished his call boosted Billy's confidence that he was doing the right thing. Now he was eager to talk to his parents – especially Mom. But what would he say? More than anything, he wanted to say, "I'm sorry," but how could he express the depth of his remorse?

Something still did not seem right about this whole set-up. His time in prison taught him to be wary of anything that promised to be free. What was the catch? Would he be asked to sign something that would put him in bondage for the rest of his life? Especially when two people in front of him left the line, suspicion prompted Billy to leave too. After waiting this long, though, he decided to stick it out. If asked to sign anything, he would refuse and leave.

In one way, the line was moving too slowly. In another way, it was moving too fast. Realizing that he would soon be seated in the chair beside Pastor Kurt sent quivers through his stomach. What if he were to become ill? Suppose Mom was already on the other end of the line when Billy had to make a mad dash for a bathroom!

With only a few people ahead of him, Billy's emotions vacillated. One moment he wanted to run but the next moment he longed to hear Mom's voice. When a woman ahead of him sat down beside Pastor Kurt, Billy's pulse quickened because he was next in line. He listened intently to the conversation.

"My mom will probably hang up on me," the woman said nervously.

Billy had never thought of that possibility although he realized such treatment would be well-deserved. Of course Mom and Dad were never unkind to anyone; so he need not concern himself about their response. He need only to worry about what he would say.

The woman on the phone started out crying but ended up laughing. Pastor Kurt seemed to empathize with her every emotion. Billy felt a connection with Pastor Kurt that eased the loneliness that had become his constant companion. It was good to be with someone who cared.

Billy stepped forward to hear the greeting, "Hi, my name is Pastor Kurt. Won't you have a seat?"

"I'm Billy," he said as he extended his hand to return the greeting. With his head down, Pastor Kurt was wiping the telephone. The pastor did not see the gesture until Billy dropped his arm. "I'm sorry," Pastor Kurt said, "but I had to disinfect the phone to make sure it was safe for you to make your call." Noting the grimy appearance of most of the people in the crowd, Billy was glad for the precautionary measure.

By now, Billy's nerves were on edge, but Pastor Kurt was as calm and unhurried as though they were the only two people in the world. Expecting Pastor Kurt to hand him the phone, Billy once again allowed his parents' telephone number to run through his mind. During the past several years, the number had run through his mind a million times, but now he wondered if he was too shaky to punch in the numbers. Pastor Kurt kept the cell phone and said, "What number do you want me to call?"

After the words stumbled out, Billy said, "Oh, man, I hope that's right."

Billy's emotions mounted. He could not tell whether his high was from nervousness or excitement. He wondered why no one was answering the phone. "It's taking too long," he whispered.

As he hung up the phone, Pastor Kurt said, "The number has been discontinued. Are you sure it was the right number?"

"Maybe I said it wrong because I was so nervous." They tried again with the same results.

"I'll call information to see if they have a new number," Pastor Kurt said. "How long has it been since you called your parents?"

Speaking in barely a whisper, Billy said, "It's been a long ... long time."

When Pastor Kurt had information on the line, he handed the phone to Billy. No matter what suggestion Billy had for finding his parents, the answer was, "Sorry. No listing." When people in the line realized they were trying to locate family, they started to complain.

"Hey, this isn't the Missing Persons Bureau," someone yelled. Pastor Kurt acknowledged the complaint with a raised hand and a smile. At that moment Billy felt like he was the most important person in the world to the pastor.

When Billy ran out of ideas, he sighed and handed the phone to Pastor Kurt. "No luck. What do we do now?"

Pastor Kurt seemed as determined as Billy was to find the young man's parents. "How about relatives?" Kurt asked. "Aunts? Uncles? Cousins? If you know where they live, we can call information and find them."

"Great idea. Let's try." By now Billy was desperate to learn anything about his family.

After several failed tries, the operator said, "I'll connect you with that number."

With sparks of anticipation in his eyes as he waited, Billy said to Kurt, "It's my uncle. He'll know what goes with my parents."

"Uncle Rudy," Billy said when a male voice answered.

"Yeah. Who's this?" Before Billy could answer, recognition registered in the older man's voice. "Billy? It's Greta's boy Billy," he said to someone who was apparently in the room.

"Yeah, Uncle Rudy. I'm living in Atlanta now." He would try to avoid speaking about his past.

"What are you doing in Atlanta?"

"I've been working at a job for a while, and I'm doing okay."

"That's good to hear. Your parents were worried about you."

"I tried to call them but the phone has been disconnected. Can you fill me in on their whereabouts?"

Uncle Rudy's silence on the other end sent throbs through Billy's head. Finally, he cleared his throat and spoke, "I'm sorry, but Greta passed away less than a year ago. Cancer. She was sick for a while."

Billy's mouth went dry, but the words squeaked out. "What about Dad?"

"I don't really know. After your mom died, he didn't communicate much with any of us. Then one day he just up and left the area and no one has heard from him since."

Too devastated to continue the conversation, Billy mumbled his thanks and goodbyes and handed the phone to Pastor Kurt. Taking hold of Billy's hand, Pastor Kurt said, "Do you want to talk about it?"

With his head hung low, Billy murmured, "It's too late. Mom's gone and no one knows where Dad is. Shaking his head and lowering his voice even further, he whispered, "I can never tell Mom

76

I'm sorry or that I love her. She'll never know."

Numbed by the shock of his loss, Billy stood up in a daze. As he wondered what to do next, Pastor Kurt stood up and placed an arm around Billy's shoulder. "I'm so sorry, Billy," he said. "I hope you'll come back to see me should you feel like talking and praying. I'm here for you whenever you need me. In fact, I'll be here again tomorrow."

Aimlessly, Billy began to walk away. Where should he go? What should he do? ... Oh, yes, he needed to head for work. On the way to Majestic Diner, Billy kept rhythm with his steps by repeating in his mind, too late ... too late ... too late ...

As Billy began to process what happened in terms of his future, a myriad of questions invaded his mind. Where could he find strength to go on? What would serve as an incentive for starting a new life now? He could never, ever, ever make things right with his parents. One summer, when Billy was little, he had attended a Vacation Bible School in the neighborhood. He remembered hearing the story of the Prodical Son. Now he could never return home and bring happiness to his parents.

Pulling more of the Bible story from his subconscious, Billy realized that the boy returned home while he was still messed up. He didn't wait to first straighten up his life. Why did I wait? he asked himself. Why, oh why, did I wait?

His head throbbed with pain as his thoughts turned to his parents. Was Dad still alive? Where was he? How was he doing? And Mom. How much did she suffer with the cancer? Did she die peacefully? The next thought sent his mind in a whirl and his knees turned to rubber. He had to lean against a post to regain his balance. No doubt Mom went to her grave heartbroken by her son's poor choices.

When he got to the diner, Billy was still early for his shift, but he did not feel like working just yet. Brushing aside his co-workers' greetings, which he usually returned with an enthusiastic response and a friendly smile, he walked with his head down and headed straight for the coffee. To avoid interaction with anyone, Billy took his coffee to a table where he sat facing a brick wall. From time to time he took a sip of coffee but, most of the time, he just sat with his head slumped down. Oblivious to the questioning glances of co-workers, Billy tried in vain to still disturbing emotions.

Unaware of time that had passed, a startled Billy looked up into the face of his boss, who had tapped him on the shoulder. "I know something is wrong, Billy. Do you want to talk about it?"

Billy just shook his head. Clem persisted, "What happened?"

Scratching his head, Billy said, "Family stuff." Never before had he mentioned his family. Conversations about family always made him nervous. If anyone asked questions, he would change the subject.

"I see." The boss paused before he asked, "Do you need to go home? We can cover for you tonight – and all weekend if necessary."

"No! No!" The sharp tone of his voice invited stares from others in the restaurant. In a softer tone, he said, "No, I need to work. I'll go crazy if I can't work." This time, he was not even thinking of the monetary benefit. In response to Clem's questioning expression, he added, "I will be fine. I promise."

"All right. Go to it."

With an apron tied around his waist, Billy handed a menu to a couple who had just sat down at a table. "Welcome to Majestic Diner," he said. "Could I get you something to drink?" It was all he could do to paste a plastic smile on his face.

"Just water for now," they both indicated as their eyes scanned the menu. With a frown on her face, the woman asked, "How's the meatloaf?"

Memory of one of his favorite childhood meals made it hard for Billy to say, "Very good. It's our special."

"I'll have the meatloaf," the lady said.

"Make it two."

Unable to put his heart into anything, Billy still found he was able to function simply by following his usual routine. When there were no customers, he kept busy cleaning the counters, the cupboards, the refrigerator – anything to chase the demons from his mind. Would that be the only way he could cope with circumstances the rest of his life?

The restaurant was empty and Billy was mopping the floor when Clem said, "Billy, it's time to go home. Your shift has ended."

The thought of going home to an empty apartment brought Billy to a near panic. He had to work to keep a semblance of sanity. At home he could only stare at the drab walls and think about his lost opportunity to make things right with his family. Anger at himself would consume him, and he would sink into the pit of depression from which he might never recover.

"Let me stay a little while longer," he pleaded.

"All right, Billy," Clem said with sympathy ringing in his voice.

Turning bolder, Billy said, "In fact, I'd like to work all day tomorrow. Let someone stay home who needs to celebrate Mother's Day with family. Let me work."

After looking over the schedule, the boss said, "Cindy likes to have holidays off, but I had to schedule her for tomorrow. I'm sure she'll be glad to have you cover for her." Noting Billy's grimy hands as he scoured the oven, Clem said, "Finish up with what you're doing and then head for home. You need to get some sleep."

By the time he finished cleaning the oven, Billy could hardly stand up from physical and emotional exhaustion. The shiny chrome on the stove, though, gave him a sense of satisfaction. He was ready to put the problems of life on hold and call it a day.

On the bus Billy checked out the place where Pastor Kurt had set up his operation. The area was now empty. He hoped many people connected with their mothers before it was too late.

Nearing his bus stop, Billy pulled the cord, got off the bus, and walked home. Without even removing his clothes, he jumped into bed and fell fast asleep.

Chapter 8

Marlene - Saturday before Mother's Day

Marlene wasn't surprised to see Pastor Kurt sitting on the sidewalk with a sign on his truck that read, "Call your mother for Mother's Day–FREE." That was the kind of thing he did to make life better for people who lived on the street. A few years back Marlene was sick and had no way to get help. "Call Pastor Kurt," a friend suggested to her. Most of the homeless had his private cell number.

Pastor Kurt had, not only referred her to an agency that provided medical assistance, he also prayed for her. Any time she needed food or clothes, she could go to Pastor Kurt for help. Just knowing that he was there for her gave her a sense of security.

Apparently, though, Pastor Kurt was not as concerned about his own security as he was about the welfare of others. Why did he choose to set up shop in the worst part of town? she wondered. Of all people, he should know about the bad stuff that went on here.

The man sitting beside Pastor Kurt was talking on the phone; so Marlene walked up to him to say hello.

"Hi, Marlene," the pastor responded. "How are you doing today?"

Shrugging her shoulders, she said, "Okay. Same as usual, I guess."

"Have you called your mother for Mother's Day yet?" the pastor asked.

"No." Calling home was hard on her emotions. It was sweet to hear the voices of her mother and two daughters, but knowing that she had let them down pierced her heart.

"Tomorrow is Mother's Day, you know. Come on. Get in line to call your mom," Pastor Kurt urged.

"All right," she agreed and went to stand in back of the line. The thought of waiting in line with all those people made her uneasy. Violence could break out at any moment and she would be right in the middle of it. The frightened woman got out of line and walked up to Pastor Kurt. "I've decided to make the call another time, but thanks anyway," she said.

The pastor was busy with the next caller, so he merely nodded and waved to her.

When she was only a few blocks away, thoughts of home began to nag at Marlene. It had been some time since she had made that call. For years she had tried to call every month. With Mother's Day coming up and all, she really should make that call. Thoughts of the kind of mother she had been to her daughters, though, made her want to forget Mother's Day forever. Her mind went back and forth. The longing to hear her daughters say, "Mommy," finally won out, and she headed back to the parking lot.

The line was longer than ever now but Marlene didn't have anything better to do, so she took her place behind a myriad of others waiting to call home. As effects of her last fix wore off, Marlene began to reminisce about her childhood.

By the time Marlene finished her reverie, she was next in line after the person making a call. Pastor Kurt looked up and said, "Oh, hi, Marlene. I'm glad you came back. You'll really make Mother's Day for your mom."

Marlene didn't want to get emotional before she even made the call; so she changed the subject. "Pastor Kurt, why are you doing this? Why did you set up in the worst part of the city?"

Pastor Kurt grinned and shrugged his shoulders. "I don't know," he said. "It was God's idea. You'll have to ask Him."

Fat chance God would give me an answer, Marlene thought.

When Pastor Kurt handed the phone to Marlene, she heard Brittany's voice. "Mommy! Mommy! I want to talk to Mommy. Is that you, Mommy?"

This wasn't going well. Already Marlene had tears in her eyes. With her daughter's words tugging at her heart, how could she keep the conversation casual? "Yes, Sweetheart, this is Mommy."

"I love you, Mommy."

"I love you too." Words could not express the emotion that seemed to swell up her head to twice its normal size.

Marlene turned to Pastor Kurt. "How long can I talk?"

"As long as you need to. Talk as long as you want."

Marlene heard how Brittany was doing in school and things the children did with Grandma. How she longed to hold both of her children close. Brittany asked, "When are you coming home, Mommy? We miss you and want you here."

Although the tears began to flow, Marlene spoke from her heart, "Mommy is coming home soon. I will get some help and come home. Mommy loves you so much."

Marlene talked to Ashley and then to her mother. To each of them she promised to come home soon. How this would happen she did not know. In fact, deep down she knew she probably never would go home.

By the time she finished the call, Marlene was sobbing. She hurriedly gave the phone to Pastor Kurt and started to leave. Grabbing her by the arm, Pastor Kurt said, "Any time, any day you want to call your kids, I want you to look me up and you can use my phone." Pastor Kurt paused as he wiped the tears from his eyes. "When you are ready to go home, Marlene, let me know. I will take you home back to your girls."

Blinking back the tears, she said, "I might call a lot."

"That's fine as long as your kids get to hear from their mother. Call every day if you want."

Almost in disbelief at the offer, she asked, "You promise?"

"I promise," Pastor Kurt said.

Too stunned to move, Marlene waited until the next caller was busy on the phone. On impulse, she reached behind her neck to her precious necklace. "Pastor Kurt, this is the most valuable thing I own. It's my birth stone and someone very special gave it to me years ago. I don't want to part with it, but calling my kids is the most important thing in the world to me. I'm giving you this necklace to remind you that you promised that I can call my kids any time I want." Marlene then hugged Pastor Kurt and took off.

As she walked along the street, Marlene felt of the empty place on her neck. It would serve as a reminder that she needed to find something else to fill the empty space in her life. Could God be the answer? she wondered.

Chapter 9

David - On Mother's Day

The following morning David woke up with enthusiasm for the day. He found only half of a piece of soggy toast in a dumpster, but he left it there. Today, eating breakfast didn't matter. Soon he would have his reward money and he would buy a half-pound cheeseburger and a chocolate malt – maybe French fries too.

With no way to tell the time, David decided to get an early start. He didn't want to be late for such an important date. He had to wash Pastor Kurt's truck. It was another perfect day and David enjoyed the walk to the parking lot where he had to meet Pastor Kurt. He could hardly wait to find out exactly how much money he would get for his hard work. If today would be half as good as yesterday, David thought, it would be great.

The parking lot was vacant when David arrived, but Pastor Kurt pulled up in his truck a few minutes later. He got out of the truck and flashed David a bright smile. "Glad to see you this morning, David." The pastor embraced David with a hug that lasted longer than usual. "It's going to be a big day, David, and I'm not quite ready for the crowd. Maybe you can help me."

86

"Okay." They got the signs out of the truck and taped them to the windshield and the rear window. Pastor Kurt asked David to set up the two chairs, but then he had him move them three times. If washing the truck was so important, why didn't they go to it? When the pastor started to walk around the block, David walked over to him and asked, "What are you doing? Where are you going?"

"I'm asking God to bless everyone who comes here today."

"Oh." David began to walk alongside. They were halfway around the parking lot when David decided to remind the pastor of their deal. "Pastor Kurt, do you want me to wash your truck today?"

"Yes, I do. We'll get to it right away."

His anxiety growing, David said, "You ... you're going to give me a big reward?"

"Yes, David, a very big reward, but the truck has to be spotless."

Curiosity prompted the question that was uppermost in his mind. "How much exactly is a big reward?"

Pastor Kurt just smiled. "I can't tell you that, David. It's a surprise. You'll just have to wait and see." The answer satisfied David for the moment because he liked surprises.

The man who seemed so eager to get his truck washed sure took his time bringing out a five-gallon bucket, a sponge, towels, and some laundry soap.

People began to gather to make their calls. One man walked up to David. "Is it really true that we can make a call for free?"

87

"Yes, you can call your mother. I called mine yesterday. Today I'm here to wash Pastor Kurt's truck." It boosted David's self-esteem to be able to give out information.

Pastor Kurt was already helping people make their calls. David put the soap and towels in the bed of the truck and waited patiently until the pastor could break away during a lengthy call. "Where will I get the water to wash the truck?" he asked.

"You'll need to go to the gas station down the street to get some water. Do you know where it is?"

David nodded. The gas station was quite a distance away but he was used to walking. As he picked up the bucket, Pastor Kurt pressed some bills into David's hand. "While you're at the gas station, buy yourself a donut and a cup of coffee. There is a Krispy Kreme nearby. You'll need the energy to wash my truck."

"Wow!" Quickly his enthusiasm vanished as he stared at three one-dollar bills in his hand. "Is this a big reward?" He was hungry and knew where the donut shop was and he was glad to be able to get something to eat. But ...

With amusement in his voice, Pastor Kurt said, "No, David, your reward will be much more valuable than this, but you have to come back and do a perfect job before you can receive it."

"Okay."

The pastor put a hand on each of David's shoulders and looked him right in the eye. "David, I'm counting on you," he said. "Please don't let me down. I need you to come back and do what you promised."

With a grin on his face, David said, "I will." The urgency in Pastor Kurt's voice surprised David but it made him feel that he was about to do something very important.

On the way to the gas station, David kept up a fast pace. The sooner he got the job done, the sooner he could collect his big reward. He kept dreaming about how he would spend the money. Maybe he would even take in a movie, although he wanted to save most of it for burgers and shakes. Oh, yes, he would use some of the money to call home. That way he wouldn't have to steal a cell phone. Stealing always made him feel really bad.

At the donut shop David laid out the three dollars on the counter. "Is this enough for a cup of coffee and a donut?" he asked.

"Yes. You can even have a large coffee and two donuts."

"I'll take it." He was beginning to feel the effects of missing breakfast and he had a lot of work to do before Pastor Kurt would give him the surprise of his life.

When he picked up the bucket filled with water, David said to himself, Man that's heavy! He began to pour out water until it was a few inches from the top, but the bucket was still heavy – heavier than the plastic bags full of aluminum cans he sometimes turned in for cash.

With the heavy load, David's walk back to the truck was slower than before. Every time he tried to hurry, some water spilled out. A time or two he even had to put the bucket down and stretch his arms. By the time he arrived back at the truck, about half of the water was gone. He hoped it would be enough to wash the truck as he would hate to have to return to the gas station for more water.

"Glad to see you back, David," Pastor Kurt said. "After the long trip, maybe you'd like to sit and rest a while."

A break was welcome but, before long, the thought of the surprise that awaited him made him eager to get on with the job.

As David rubbed the soapy sponge over the car, removal of the grime allowed the green paint to shine through. Because the truck was close to the chairs where Pastor Kurt and the callers sat, David could hear most of the conversations. It made the time go faster. The happy voices and the smiles on people's faces gave David a warm feeling inside. Other people left with tears and solemn faces and David shared their sorrow.

Every time he could break away from the phone, Pastor Kurt came over to give David a few words of praise. The encouragement made him want to do an even better job. When he saw people he knew in line, David hoped they would notice that he had a part in this important mission.

A short while later, the water was so filthy that his attempt at washing a dirty area left muddy streaks. Only part of the job was finished. David went over and over an area but he could not remove the streaks. He was not surprised when Pastor Kurt said, "I'm afraid we're going to have to get some clean water, David."

"Yeah." David paused and looked around at the crowd. "Pastor Kurt, this is awesome – the phone calls and all. I'll get going and be back to finish my part."

All the way to the gas station, David dreaded the trip back with the heavy pail of water. This time he filled the bucket only half full because that was all he would end up with anyway. The job was turning out to require more effort than David expected, but he was determined to do his best.

Back at the job David tried to hurry. He knew about a mission that served an early dinner. Maybe he could finish in time to get the free meal. That way he could save the money from Pastor Kurt until he was really hungry. Of course he would have to worry that someone might beat him up and steal his money. Mom and Dad used to keep their money in a bank but David had never before had enough money to be concerned about. Where could he keep his money safe? He would remember to put the question to Pastor Kurt.

When David announced that he had finished the job, the pastor put his arm on David's shoulder. "It looks great, David. You did a wonderful job – except around the wheels. It's hard to get all the corners but I know you can do it."

David worked until the wheels were gleaming but Pastor Kurt continued to point out spots on the truck. Why was he being so picky? David wondered.

All the while people were lined up to make their calls, cars going by slowed down. The drivers were trying to figure out what was going on. Did that mean trouble? David wondered. He never understood why, but some people were out to get Pastor Kurt. The pastor was very brave and he could take care of himself, although he always said that God protected him for a purpose. David had heard that the pastor had several knives and even guns that people had used to try to hurt him. "God protects me because He loves you through me," Pastor Kurt sometimes said. The explanation always made David feel good.

Every eye in the line was turned toward the car that was moving closer to Pastor Kurt's truck. Suddenly David dropped the sponge and yelled, "Mom," as he ran toward the woman getting out of the car. For the moment, all he wanted was to remain locked in her embrace. When Dad tapped him on the shoulder, David released Mom with his left arm and included Dad in the gang hug.

Applause erupted from the crowd. David smiled and waved. This was like a scene from a movie and David was the star. He couldn't remember ever being so happy.

After the excitement died down, David was full of questions. "How did you find me?" he asked.

"Let's go talk to Pastor Kurt. We need to thank him for his help," Dad said. David did not understand what Pastor Kurt did to help them, but he went along with his parents.

Dad extended his hand to the pastor. "You have our undying gratitude," he said. "David has been gone a long time, but we never stopped looking for him and longing to see him."

"I couldn't promise anything but I'm glad it worked out," Pastor Kurt said.

With tears streaming down her face, Mom hugged the pastor. "Thank you, thank you, thank you," she repeated several times.

"Thank the Lord. I just put the situation in God's hands and God worked it out."

Confused, David asked, "What are you all talking about? What did Pastor Kurt do?"

"I'm not sure how he did it, but he kept you. We came as quickly as we could."

"But how did you know ... I heard Pastor Kurt talking to you. He didn't tell you where I was."

"When he called, his number showed up on our phone. We called him that evening to make arrangements," Mom explained.

Casting an accusing look toward Pastor Kurt, David said, "That's why you had me wash your truck and I had to do a perfect job."

"That's right, David."

To his parents, David said, "You went to all of that trouble just to come and see me?"

"It's more than that, David. We've come to take you home with us," Mom said as she gave her son yet another hug, "that is if you want to."

David released his arms and backed away. His joy from seeing his parents became clouded with fear. "Do I have to go to school?"

"No, David. You never have to go to school again. Either your father or I will be with you all the time," Mom promised.

Pastor Kurt quickly took David by the hand and looked squarely into his eyes. "David, you don't have to go if you don't want to."

A smile spread clear across David's face and he began to jump up and down. "All right! Let's go home."

The next person in line was ready to make a call, but Pastor Kurt held up his hand to give his attention to David. "Don't ever forget, David. God loves you and so do I."

"I'll remember."

Mom and Dad both had a hand on David's shoulder as they walked to the car. Mom sat in the middle and David sat in the passenger seat. Dad started the motor and turned around in the parking lot. As soon as the thought popped into his mind, David held up his hand. "Wait, Dad, wait! Roll down the window. I need to say something to Pastor Kurt."

Dad pulled forward. David stuck his head out the window. "Pastor Kurt," he called. "What about the money for washing your truck? The reward?"

With a smile on his face, Pastor Kurt said, "How much do you need for a big reward?"

David looked at his family sitting beside him. Laughing, he said, "Are you kidding? This is my reward."

As they headed for home, David realized what he received today was far bigger than anything he could ever have imagined.

Chapter 10

Billy - On Mother's Day

When he opened his eyes to look at the clock, Billy tried to coax his brain to shut down so he could go back to sleep. Certainly his body needed rest but his mind would not cooperate. All night long scenes from his past flashed through his mind. Like the time when he came home from school crying because his bicycle had been stolen. He had saved his allowance for months to buy the bicycle but it was snatched away in a moment.

Mom climbed up on a stool and took down the jar where she always put away any money that was left over after the bills were paid. "We'll take out whatever you need to buy you a new bicycle," Mom said as she started grouping like bills together.

Surprised by Mom's action, Billy stopped crying but he bit his lip. "Isn't that the money you are saving to buy a new stove?"

"Yes, but I can use the old one for a while longer."

At the time, Billy had mixed emotions. He really wanted the bicycle but he felt sad because Mom could not get her new stove. Soon after he got his new bike, though, he forgot all about Mom's sacrifice. Now he could never thank his mother for giving him a happy childhood. He could never thank her for baking his favorite chocolate chip cookies in the oven that she had to watch constantly because the thermostat was broken.

If he had to endure the pain of memory any longer, Billy felt he would go crazy. Work. Work was the only thing that could help him retain his sanity. Taking a double shift today as he requested would make for a long day, but maybe when he got home this time he would be able to sleep.

Still with his mind in a whirl, Billy hopped out of bed and dragged himself into the bathroom. A look at his face in the mirror said he looked as bad as he felt. Death warmed over, was the way Mom would have described him. If he couldn't come to life, Clem would send him home for fear he would drive the customers away. After filling the basin with cold water, Billy leaned over the sink. He cupped his hands and spread the cool water over his face and then proceeded to shave. With his eyes more alert and an artificial smile pasted on his face, he mouthed the words, "How can I serve you?" Today he would rely on his training to take over because there was no way he could put his heart into his work.

In the shower, Billy wished he could clean up his past with soap and water. The warm water felt good on his aching muscles. He wished he could linger longer in the relaxing spray but he knew he had to face the day. His mind turned to his goals – one of which was to save money to go home.

Savings! What did it matter now? His reason for working, his reason for saving, his reason for living had been taken away. Now there was no way he could ever prove to his family that he had turned his life around. How could he replace his goal when nothing else mattered? He might as well have stayed in jail the rest of his life.

Nothing mattered? Stay in jail? Such ideas startled him. That kind of thinking could put him behind bars again. Somehow he had to figure out a way to make life worth living. He needed a purpose to throw himself into. What could give him the incentive to try to find another reason for living? Right now he didn't have a clue as to how to get his life together, but he had to come up with something. Otherwise ... otherwise, he refused to go there.

As he put on his white shirt, Billy noticed a dark spot that looked like it might be catsup. Oh well, what difference would it make? A spot on his shirt matched his messed-up life. He did not have the heart to change.

Although he could eat at the diner, Billy needed strength to make the trip to work. The coffee at the diner was better than the instant coffee he fixed for himself, but at least the caffeine would help him stay alert. As he poured out the same cereal he had had for nearly two weeks, Billy reminded himself to get something different the next time he went to the store.

While washing his cereal bowl, Billy once again noticed the spot on his shirt. Mom would never have allowed him to leave the house in a dirty shirt. To honor the memory of Mom, he removed his shirt and washed out the spot. When he put the shirt back on, the wet spot felt cool on his skin. By the time he got to work, the shirt would be dry.

On the way to the bus, Billy noticed a patch of wild flowers growing beside the sidewalk. The beauty of the delicate pink flowers seemed out of place. Not many flowers grew in his area of town. He reached down to pick a flower and placed it in the buttonhole of his shirt. Could he somehow find a way to put beauty into his life? he wondered.

The flower reminded Billy of the landscape around his parents' house. At one time he had dreamed of someday owning a home and having a family. That dream had died when he went to prison to be replaced by his desire to redeem himself in the eyes of his parents. Could he now resurrect the dream of his youth and hope for a family of his own someday? Would he know how to guide a son to prevent him from repeating his own mistakes?

Nearing the corner where he learned the terrible truth yesterday, Billy checked to see if there was any activity. All was quiet. Pastor Kurt had said he would be back in business for Mother's Day, but it was probably too early. In any event, he had no reason to return to the scene where his heart was wrenched from his body. Although he hoped there would be many happy reunions today, he did not even want to think about Mother's Day.

Pastor Kurt had seemed to genuinely share Billy's grief. "God loves you, Billy, and so do I," he had said with tears in his eyes. He had also invited Billy to come back if he needed to talk. Right now it didn't seem like anything they could talk about would make a difference, but maybe later he would seek help in putting the broken pieces of his life back together.

Ernie, the friendly bus driver, was on the route this morning. "A good day to you, Billy Boy," he said in a cheerful tone of voice.

"Good morning, Ernie." Billy tried to sound friendly. He might as well start to practice for the day's job. Not many people were on the bus. When the seat behind the driver was empty, Billy often sat there to talk to the driver. Today he moved farther back even though the seat was open and Ernie seemed ready for conversation.

During the short ride, Billy's mind was so occupied that he failed to pull the cord at his stop. Ernie called out, "Billy, this is your stop."

"Thanks, Man." Realizing how fortunate he was to have someone looking out for him, he added, "I don't know what I'd do without you, Ernie."

When he arrived at work, Billy was glad to receive a pleasant greeting from Clem. His boss had been good to him and Billy vowed that his work would not suffer because of his personal problems.

"Are you going to be okay today?" Clem asked.

Billy nodded even as he looked around for some extra work to keep him busy. The kitchen floor was mopped every day, but it had been a long time since it had been scrubbed by hand with a brush. Determined to make Majestic Diner the cleanest restaurant in town, Billy got down on his knees and went to work with a vengeance.

Watching the grime in the grout of the tile slowly disappear fascinated him. With hard work maybe he could remove the grime from his life.

By the time a customer came into the restaurant, Billy felt more like interacting with members of the human race. The couple who sat at the table was not typical Majestic Diner clientele. Because of the diner's location, most of the customers were from the street. Although the man had obviously been beaten up, he wore an expensive suit that went along with the luxury car parked outside.

In response to Billy's friendly greeting as he placed glasses of water on the table, only the woman replied. "We won't order anything to eat," she said. "Just strong coffee and tomato juice for my husband. He needs to sober up."

While coaxing her husband to drink the coffee and tomato juice, the wife filled Billy in on the details. The successful business man had stayed too long at the bar, got lost trying to find his car, and ended up in the wrong place where he was robbed and beaten. The police contacted his wife to come and rescue him. "I took a neighbor along with me to drive his car back home," she said.

After the couple left, Billy handed the generous tip over to Clem to be entered in the books and later included in his paycheck.

As Billy went back to scrubbing the floor, he continued to muse about the story he had just heard. To him, it had an ironic twist that was almost laughable. The story began in an affluent society but it ended up just like everyone else on the street. Apparently it isn't necessary to be down and out to get your life messed up.

"The floor is clean enough to eat on now," Billy said to Clem when he finished the job.

"It looks great, but it's time for a break. Let's sit down with a cup of coffee."

The suggestion sounded good to Billy. The emotional roller coaster he had been on for the past twenty-four hours was beginning to catch up with him. Somehow he had to find relief soon.

"We probably won't be very busy today," Clem said as they sat looking out the window sipping coffee. "Majestic Diner isn't exactly the kind of place anyone would want to take Mom to celebrate Mother's Day."

At the mention of Mother's Day, Billy's words began to pour out. He explained what Pastor Kurt was doing and how he had mixed emotions about calling his mother. "When I finally got up nerve enough to call her, I learned that she had passed away. I'll never be able to make right all the things I did wrong." Billy was so near tears he had to retreat to the bathroom to compose himself.

When Billy returned to the table, Clem said, "Learning of your mother's death was quite a blow. You're bound to have regrets, but you're back on track now, Billy. Just honor your mom with the rest of your life, and that should bring you peace."

As furrows of thought registered on his brow, Billy picked up his spoon and stirred his coffee even though he drank his coffee black. "Thanks for listening and for your kind words," he said.

A young man came in. Billy guessed he was still in his teens.

When asked what he would like to drink, the boy said, "Just water." His hand shook as he reached for the menu. After studying the menu, he counted the money in his wallet. The customer was obviously a troubled young man.

With no one else in the diner, Billy tried to engage the boy in conversation. Pointing to his name tag, he said, "I'm Billy. What's your name?"

Without looking up from the menu, the boy said, "Brett."

"Where are you from, Brett?"

As Brett raised his eyes, Billy could see a look of fear that was all too familiar to him. "Uh ... uh ..." Brett stammered. "Uh ... I'm on my way to Florida." Turning his attention to the menu, he said, "I think I'll have the grilled pork chop with sweet potatoes and fried apples."

"A good choice." Billy turned the order in to Clem and then returned to Brett's table.Noting the absence of a car in front of the diner, Billy asked, "How will you get to Florida?"

"Hitchhiking." Billy was able to learn that a man traveling down I-75 from Knoxville, Tennessee had stopped at the nearby gas station and then turned off to another route. Although he had often used the last-resort method of transportation himself, Billy began to warn Brett of the dangers of hitchhiking.

"Sometimes you have to do what you have to do," Brett said.

For a moment Billy considered Brett's words, wondering how to respond. Finally, he said, "Do you really have to go to Florida?"

"Yes," the boy shot back as his eyes made contact with Billy. He then lowered his eyes and said, "Well, no – not really." The story paralleled Billy's past. His parents objected to the company their son was keeping, but Brett would not give them up. When some of his friends moved to Florida, Brett decided to join them.

The bell rang, indicating that Brett's meal was ready. After serving the meal, Billy refilled the boy's water glass and then busied himself in the kitchen.

A short while later Billy returned to ask Brett, "How is everything?"

"Great. Everything tastes just like my mother's cooking."

"Today is Mother's Day, you know. Have you called your mother?"

The boy shook his head. The look of sadness that came over Brett's face caused Billy to ask, "Do your parents know where you are?"

"I left a note but I didn't tell them where I was going."

The words aroused a strong passion in Billy. Anger consumed his emotions. He simply would not allow to continue the course of events already in motion. The story had to take a different turn, but how? He wanted to stand up and fight. With that thought in mind, he grabbed the table, leaned his football linebacker frame over the table and faced Brett with fire in his eyes. Although he wanted to lash out at the boy, no words came. His very presence, though, frightened the boy.

Startled by his own boldness that could get him fired if a confrontation erupted, Billy backed off. Who was he to act as the poster child for a good son, anyway? Compassion began to replace his rage. What could he do to get the message through to the boy? Although he wasn't used to praying for anyone but himself, he began to pray for Brett. "God, show me what I can say that would help," he prayed.

An idea came to Billy's mind. "The note," he said. "Would you want the note to be the last communication you ever have with your parents? Can you imagine what it would be like to never again taste your mother's cooking?"

Tears filled the boy's eyes. "No..... I want to live my own life, my own way. I will get back in touch with my parents later."

"You may not have that opportunity." In a very poignant manner, Billy related his own story to Brett. He finished with the words, "How I miss Mom and Dad. If I had it, I'd give a million dollars just to hear them give me a lecture on right and wrong. Just to be with them would be enough."

After Brett paid his bill, he counted out change for the tip. Billy handed it back with the words, "Keep the tip and use it to call your mother."

Brett hesitated before he said, "All right, I will."

Billy dug in his pocket and pulled out five quarters and two dimes. "Take this, too. Talk to her as long as you can."

"Thanks. Thanks for everything."

The telephone booth was visible from the diner. With great interest Billy watched Brett's tears gradually turn to a smile. When he finished, he gave Billy a "high five" wave and pointed North.

When Billy began to hum a tune in the kitchen, Clem said, "I see your mood is improving."

"Yeah, it's hard to believe isn't it?" Already he felt happier than he had believed possible this morning. Maybe it was his purpose in life to help others avoid the mistakes he had made. If he could do some good in the world, perhaps he could give God a reason to love him as Pastor Kurt said He did. Pastor Kurt had told Billy that he would be there for him any time he needed help. It would be good to learn more about this God who loved him even when he was unlovable.

An older couple walked into the restaurant followed by a seemingly frightened woman. She was probably the couple's daughter, although it was hard to tell her age from her disheveled appearance. In spite of the tough look of the streets, she had obviously been crying. What kind of a Mother's Day celebration was in store for this family? Billy wondered.

As he approached their table with a menu in hand, Billy wondered if he would have another opportunity to work on his life's purpose.

Chapter 11

Erica - On Mother's Day

While walking to the corner gas station to buy cigarettes, Erica noticed the sign, "Call your mother for Mother's Day–FREE." Thoughts of her mother put Erica's mind in a whirl. It had been a long time since she had contacted her parents. Scenes of the journey from her home to here flashed through her mind.

There had been no contact with her family for more than a year. Now she stood looking at a sign that said, "Call your mother for Mother's Day–FREE." With a laugh, Erica thought, if I call my mother, it has to be for free. She had to scrounge around in her room to find enough change for cigarettes.

Squelching an overwhelming urge to call her parents, Erica went on to the gas station. She had to have cigarettes before she could consider doing anything else. The decision would have to wait until she returned.

When Erica returned from the gas station, the line for the free calls was longer than ever. Since she didn't have anything else to do, she joined the line while puffing on a cigarette. She had often wondered how her mom and dad would deal with her life's decisions.

Would they disown her? Actually, they had good reason to reject her. She had a hard time accepting herself. Still, she had hoped her parents would support her no matter what. Well, she would soon find out where she stood with her family.

A myriad of thoughts ran through Erica's mind as she stood in the long line. Who was offering the free phone call and why? What was the catch? Most organizations wanted to make money. Maybe the phone was provided but everyone had to pay for the call plus a fee. If that were the case, she would get around it somehow. Now that she was in the mood, she would make that call even if she had to throw a tantrum and make an ugly scene.

When she tried to rehearse the conversation, Erica was not so sure of herself. Should she first apologize for not calling in a year? Should she tell them how messed up she was or just ignore what she had been doing for several years?

Oh well, she whispered to herself, I'll just let what happens happen. I just miss my mom and dad.

The line moved slowly and Erica had smoked almost all of her cigarettes. She had hoped they would last long enough to call her family. In the crowd of homeless and poor people, she knew the chances of getting a free smoke were slim.

With this many people on the street, it was surprising that everyone remained respectful and orderly. Perhaps others were also pondering what they would say to their mothers. Certainly she was not alone in her situation. Others looked as though they had made some wrong choices too.

As she grew closer to the sign, Erica recognized it was Pastor Kurt with the cell phone. She knew him from the outdoor church services he had around town. His presence made her feel at ease because he really cared about people. He never talked "down" to them.

Only five people were ahead of Erica now. Instead of wishing the line would move faster, she now wished it would move slower. Her heart pounded so hard she wondered if she would be able to talk. When one of the men ahead of her decided to turn away, Erica understood. Staying in line was one of the scariest things she had done in a long time.

Pastor Kurt cleaned the phone and made the call for the woman in front of her. A moment later the woman handed the phone back to the pastor and left with her head hanging low. Was no one at home? Did someone hang up? ... Would she, too, be disappointed when she made the call? Erica wondered. Life would be too hard to bear if she could never again hear her parents say, "I love you."

The call from Pastor Kurt interrupted Erica's thoughts. Sitting beside the pastor, she nervously waited while he cleaned the phone. When he asked who she wanted to call, she said, "My mom and dad" as she grabbed for the phone.

"Wait," Pastor Kurt said. "Let me make the call and introduce myself, and then I'll hand you the phone."

The phone rang three times before the pastor said, "This is Pastor Kurt from Church On The Street. Your daughter is here and wants to wish you happy Mother's Day." Handing the phone to Erica, Pastor Kurt said, "Take as much time as you need."

With trembling hands, Erica took the phone. "Mom, Dad, are you there?" she said.

"We're both on the phone," Mom said.

"Happy Mother's Day." Erica's voice cracked with emotion.

"It's been so long since we've heard from you," Mom said.

"I know. I'm so sorry, but ... A lot has happened here." Erica tried to make the story of her life sound plausible without revealing what caused her downfall.

Dad interrupted her words with pleas for her to return home. Dad spoke sternly and Mom was crying. Finally, Dad said, "Let me talk to Pastor Kurt."

As the man in the clerical collar took the phone, Erica wished she could listen in on the conversation. She could tell nothing from the pastor's end. He merely said, "Yes ... I'll try ... I'll do my best." If she could only fill in the blanks with her father's words.

When Pastor Kurt handed the phone back, Erica heard the words she had longed to hear. "I love you too, Mom and Dad," she said with tears in her eyes. "I will be here when you come."

After saying goodbye, Erica held onto the phone and tried to gain her composure while still seated. The man next in line called out impatiently, "It's my turn. It's my turn."

Gently taking the phone from Erica, Pastor Kurt said, "I have to make the call for the next person, but stick around and we can talk.

Your mom and dad want to come see you."

As Erica stood up, her head was in a whirl. To steady herself, she leaned against the truck with the sign, "Call your mother for Mother's Day–FREE." That sign had certainly caused a dramatic turn in her life.

While the man talked with his family, Pastor Kurt got up and gave Erica a hug. With one arm, she hugged him back while keeping one arm on the truck to balance herself. Then she dissolved into tears. "They want me to come home," she said.

"Do you want to go home?"

"I don't know.... I don't know."

"I'm hungry," Pastor Kurt said.

Startled by the words that seemed out of place, Erica said, "What?" Her heart had just been pulled from her chest and the man of God was only concerned about his stomach. Anger flared up inside of her.

"Erica, could you please get us something to eat down the road? I've been here all afternoon and I'm really hungry." While Erica stared at the strange man, he dug into his pocket and pulled out a ten-dollar bill, which he handed to the distraught girl. Pointing in the opposite direction of the closest restaurant, Pastor Kurt said, "There's a restaurant just down the road that makes great sandwiches. Could you please get us something to eat? We can talk after you get back."

Clinging to the money, Erica stood in stunned silence. She certainly did not know what to make of the unusual behavior of the man who had seemed so normal before.

"I really need that sandwich. Will you get it for me?" When Erica made no response, he gave her another hug and said, "Would you rather talk now?"

She shook her head. What was up with this guy? she wondered. Well, she decided she might as well play along. Besides, she was hungry too. He had told her she could eat her sandwich at the restaurant and bring his back. At least the distraction might help her quit thinking about the phone call with her parents. "Where do you want me to get the sandwiches?" she asked.

The pastor gave her detailed directions to the restaurant that was hard to find. He also had specific instructions as to how his sandwich should be made. What a fussy eater, Erica thought. Before he finished describing the sandwich he wanted, Pastor Kurt had to clean the phone for the next caller. The man who left seemed happy, and that gave Erica a sense of peace.

While the pastor made the phone call for the next person, Erica reached in her pocket for her last cigarette. Drawing the smoke into her lungs seemed to bring her comfort.

When he finished the phone call, the pastor said, "How about it, Erica? Are you agreeable to our plan?" She continued to puff on her cigarette with a dubious expression on her face. "I'll tell you what," he said persuasively. "I need that sandwich so much that I'll give you ten dollars when you bring it back."

"Okay, I'll get the sandwiches. But why do you want me to go so far away? Other places have good food."

"I need the sandwich made that special way."

With all the instructions Pastor Kurt had given her, she figured that anyone should be able to make what he wanted, but she did not question him further. By now, she was amused by the strange turn of events.

"All right. I'm on my way," she said as she took off in the right direction.

When she was out of sight, Erica thought about her options. With the ten dollars in her hand, she could buy two rocks of crack cocaine and smoke this day away. By the time the day was over, she would not even realize that the talk with her parents had put her emotions in turmoil.

In spite of the temptation to get high, Erica kept walking toward the restaurant. As her mind replayed the conversation with her parents, she began to confuse what was actually said and what she was thinking. Did Dad say anything about coming to get her or did she dream up the idea? she wondered. Dad had talked to Pastor Kurt and Erica did not know what was said. She almost hoped he did have a good reason for his erratic behavior. At least she thought, time would go by faster. Maybe, that was Pastor Kurt's intention.

How would she react if her parents came to get her? ... Fearful! Shameful! She could only face her parents with fear and shame . . . but, oh, how she longed to love and be loved!

At the restaurant Erica put in the order for the special

112

sandwich along with her own. There was enough money left over to buy another pack of cigarettes, which she needed badly. She smoked one while waiting for the sandwiches. Her thoughts turned to the ten dollars promised by Pastor Kurt when she made it back. Maybe she would end the day with a couple of rocks of crack to relieve the emotional pain she had suffered.

Instead of eating her sandwich at the restaurant as the pastor suggested, she headed back carrying both sandwiches. Pastor Kurt's face lighted up as she approached as though he was glad to see her.

The girl who sat in the other chair was talking on the phone with a smile on her face. The scene again warmed Erica's heart. I hope she doesn't have as far to go to make things right with her family as I do, she thought. The possibility that her parents might come to get her kept nagging at Erica's mind. She longed to once again experience the love of Mom and Dad, but how could she bridge the great gap between them?

"Here's your sandwich just like you wanted it," Erica whispered to the pastor as she took out her own sandwich and handed the bag to him.

"Thank you." Pastor Kurt stood up and offered the chair to Erica.

"No. No. You need to sit there with the people who want to call home. I'll sit here on the curb." Erica was used to doing without the comforts that most people took for granted.

Pastor Kurt had removed the sandwich wrapper and was about

to take a bite when a man in line yelled, "Hey, Pastor Kurt, I'm hungry. Will you share your sandwich?" The pastor gave him half of his sandwich.

"I'm hungry too," another man yelled.

What will he do now? Erica wondered. The man of God hesitated for only a moment until he handed the man the other half of his sandwich. What's with this man? she wondered. He was hungry and had to have a sandwich made a certain way. When it comes, he gives it away. It didn't make sense. Erica turned her back to the crowd before people started asking for her sandwich. She was not so willing to share.

After finishing her sandwich, Erica stood up. Time seemed to move slowly now that she was back to the truck. Trembling from anxiety, Erica wanted to leave. The uncertainty about seeing her parents was unbearable. Suddenly, Pastor Kurt blurted out, "Erica, I need to give you the ten dollars I promised you."

Pastor Kurt went to his truck to look for the promised money. As he looked in every possible container in the truck, Erica gave him the "evil eye." Finally, he reached in his front pant pockets and pulled out a ten-dollar bill, which he handed to Erica. With pleading in his voice, he said, "Please wait for your parents to come."

With the money in her hand, Erica thought about drowning out all of the buried emotions that had been resurrected during the day. They were too painful to entertain any longer. Still, for an unexplained reason, she lingered. Without a word, she sat back on the sidewalk curled up with her chin to her knees. It had been a long time since she experienced so many conflicting emotions. Too many unanswered questions invaded her mind.

After waiting for the next caller to begin the telephone conversation, Erica said, "Pastor Kurt, will you explain something to me?"

"If I can."

"Why did you give away your sandwich when you were so hungry and I went to so much trouble to get it for you?"

A smile covered the tired expression on the pastor's face. "It's all because of Jesus," he said. Erica's face registered confusion as she did not understand what Jesus had to do with giving away his sandwich. To her questioning glance, he continued. "You see, Jesus said that when I help someone in need, it's the same as though I did it for Him. I got to give Jesus a sandwich."

Now she was totally confused. She knew the bum Pastor Kurt gave the sandwich to. He was no "Jesus." The explanation failed to satisfy Erica's curiosity, but her mind turned to another matter heavy on her mind. Even though she was afraid to hear the answer, she had to ask, "What did my dad say to you on the phone?"

When the pastor hesitated, she stared at him with anticipation.

"He told me that he loved you so much that he would do anything to see you. He said that you have run away every time they tried to see you. He wanted me to try to keep you here as long as I could. Your parents both love you, Erica."

Her suspicions were true. It seemed to be a comfort to her to know that Dad was working so hard to see her. This time, she desperately wanted to connect with her parents. Today - on Mother's Day. At the same time, her whole body shook with the thought of facing them in her condition. She feared her head might split in two with such conflicting emotions.

Pastor Kurt finally spoke. "Erica, if my calculations are correct, they should be here in about an hour. Can you make it that long?" Pastor Kurt seemed to be as emotional as Erica.

Unable to respond, with her head spinning, Erica rolled sideways on the curb in a fetal position. Her legs had turned to jelly and she could not have run away if she had wanted to. Pastor Kurt asked, "Are you all right?"

All she could do was nod her head. She knew this was going to be a long hour. Still in a daze, she raised herself up in a sitting position and watched every passing car. As the cars slowed down, people looked to see what the crowd was doing in this part of town. Erica strained to see if her parents were inside.

It had been a long time since Erica worried about her appearance. Now she wished she could wash her face and apply some makeup and comb her hair. Although she didn't notice it herself, she knew she reeked of body odor and tobacco smoke. She looked at the tattoos on her arms and legs. How she wished she could remove them, but they were there to stay.

Finally, a blue sedan drove slowly beside the line of people and toward her. It was a newer model but the same style and color of car she had ridden to school in every time it rained. Those days seemed far away.

Recognizing her parents, Erica got up and took a few steps and then broke into a run. Regardless of the consequences, she was eager to see her mom and dad. Mom opened the car door and stepped outside, but Dad remained in the car. Mother and daughter both dissolved into tears as they embraced, but neither said a word.

"Erica, get in the car. We'll catch up on everything later," Dad said. He always was the strong silent type.

After opening the back door of the car, Erica turned for another glimpse of Pastor Kurt. He was watching the scene intently and they both waved at the same time. She realized a miracle had brought her together with her family, and it would take another miracle to mend their broken relationship.

Dad had barely turned the car around when he started to pepper Erica with questions. "What have you been doing? Why haven't you kept in touch? Do you realize what you've been doing to your mother's health? She's been worried sick." The questions came one after another before Erica even had the chance to answer.

Realizing she deserved Dad's condemnation, Erica still wished he would take it easy and allow the truth to come out slowly and naturally. Interrupting Dad's tirade, she pleaded, "Dad, Mom, I know I haven't done right and I'm really sorry."

"Sorry doesn't cut it with me. I want some straight answers.

For starters, where are you working?" Dad asked.

"You know I went to work at a restaurant when I first came here."

"Are you working there now?"

"No."

"Where do you work?"

"I - I don't."

"Then how do you eat?"

"I have other sources of income."

Erica could see Dad's eyes flashing as he studied her in the rear view mirror. "Are you a prostitute, Erica?"

Lowering her eyes, Erica said, "I didn't intend to be."

"What you intended doesn't have anything to do with it. Are you or aren't you?" Dad shouted.

"Yes," Erica replied meekly.

Mom took hold of Dad's shoulder. "Jim, please stay calm," she said.

"Calm! I find out my daughter's a whore and you want me to remain calm? You're the one who's been worrying. How can you stay calm, now?"

"Please, Jim, I don't want you to have a heart attack or an accident. Why don't we pull off the road and have a cup of coffee or something?"

"There's a restaurant at the next light," Erica said in hopes of restoring order.

Without a word, Dad turned right at the light and stopped in front of Majestic Diner. As Dad got out of the car, he looked at Erica with contempt in his eyes. "I'm certainly not proud to be taking you anyplace with those tattoos all over your body," he said.

Already Erica wished she had run when she had the chance. Mom might have cut her some slack, but Dad was out for blood. As the first one into the restaurant, Erica chose a table right in the middle. Maybe being on center stage would prevent Dad from continuing to lash out at her.

"All right, explain yourself," Dad said as soon as they sat down.

Through tears and with intense emotion, she started to explain how the stranger at the party showed her the way out of her financial worries. "I was broke, Dad, with lots of bills, and I didn't know what else to do."

Dad's red face indicated that his anger had mounted. Through gritted teeth, he said, "You could have called home."

The waiter brought menus. "I'm Billy," he said. "Would you like something to drink?"

"Later," Dad said as he waved him away. To Erica, he said, "Why didn't you call home?"

"I didn't want to trouble you and I wanted to make it on my own."

"You made it on your own all right, and disgraced the family in the process."

Unable to take any more, Erica retreated to the restroom. Billy's eyes followed her movement. He had seemed to show interest in the family from the time they entered the restaurant. They looked like a family in distress.

When Erica started to leave the restroom, she abruptly changed her mind. If she stayed away long enough, maybe Dad would take off without her. If not, maybe Mom could calm him down. In an effort to remove the stress lines, she splashed water over her face and dried it with a paper towel. The tiny splash on the sink indicated tears had started flowing again. This has to stop, she told herself. To show she meant business, she gave both cheeks a quick, hard slap to shock her emotions into obedience. After dabbing her eyes with cold water, she headed back to the table.

While still in the hallway, Erica could hear Dad say, "You don't know what she's done."

Moving so she could see but not be seen, Erica saw Billy standing by the table. In response to Dad's remark, Billy grasped the edge of the table with both hands and leaned over. "I don't care what she's done," Billy said slowly and deliberately. "You're still family. I'd give everything I'll ever earn if I could have one day with my family again. Mom died a year ago. It was too late when I tried to make things right." When Billy straightened up, he was shaking.

It was as though the Holy Spirit directed Billy's words and his towering presence made an obvious impact on Dad.

Dad's face had turned from red to white. For once, he was

speechless. He had practiced what he would say a thousand times if he ever got a chance to see his daughter again. He knew he blew it. He did and said just the opposite of what he wanted to. He was ashamed of himself.

"Shall we order coffee?" Mom asked.

"Yes. Coffee."

While Billy went for the coffee, Erica headed for the table with her parents. Before she sat down, Dad stood up. In an awkward manner, he hugged Erica and said, "I'm sorry, Erica. We'll work things out. I love you and I want us to be a family again." Mom's face beamed.

The three of them sat drinking coffee in silence, but Erica was deep in thought. Pastor Kurt had said that Jesus died to pay for her sins. "When God forgives you, it's the same as though you had never sinned," he had said. With that promise, perhaps she could find a new beginning, she thought.

Chapter 12

Leonard - On Mother's Day

On the way to the crack house, Leonard noticed a sign: "Call your mother for Mother's Day–FREE." The sign created a longing in Leonard's heart. He missed his parents, especially his mother. If he called, what would he say? Five years was too long to try to bridge with a casual conversation. He couldn't just say he was sorry and let it go at that. He had too many things to say he was sorry for. It would be too embarrassing to call home and admit he was a total failure. He just couldn't do it. His only option was to continue on to the crack house and forget the sign.

Several blocks away, the words still blazed in Leonard's mind. "Call your mother for Mother's Day–FREE." He made a u-turn and walked back to take his place at the end of the line. Still, doubts kept him on edge. How could he even begin a conversation? What if his parents wanted nothing to do with him?

For several minutes, Leonard was torn between wanting to leave and wanting to stay. The desire to stay seemed stronger, but the long line ahead intimidated him. Too much time to lose his nerve. Then he had an idea. In his most charming manner, he said to the man in front of him. "Excuse me, sir. I haven't talked to my mom for a long time, but I have to be at work in a couple of hours. If you're not pushed for time, would you mind if I go ahead of you?"

Street people aren't used to granting favors. They're more interested in gaining favors. Nevertheless, the man stared at Leonard for a few moments, and then motioned for him to move forward. From then on, Leonard made a game of moving up the line.

With only two people ahead of Leonard, his anxiety returned. At that moment he noticed a necklace hanging from the rear view mirror of Pastor Kurt's truck. He was accustomed to looking into cars for things to steal and eventually sell for drugs. It was a natural response but when he stared into the truck, this time, the necklace looked familiar. Excitement rushed through his body when he realized it was just like the one he had given to a special friend many years ago. The crooked cross was accented with stones resembling rubies – the birth stone of Leonard and his friend.

Thoughts of the terrific vacations with his parents in Florida flooded his mind, erasing the doubts and confusion about calling his family. The necklace reminded him of good things and courage surged through his soul.

Tears had already welled up in his eyes by the time Pastor Kurt motioned to Leonard to sit next to him and asked what number he should call. He was too nervous to sit down, so he paced slowly around the chair during the call. He need not have worried about what to say. As soon as he addressed her by name, Mom's words began to pour out. "Leonard, Leonard, oh my boy. How we've missed you. When we didn't hear from you, we feared you were dead."

"Yeah, I'm sorry I didn't call. I wanted to, but things haven't gone too well for me. I was ashamed to let you know how bad I messed up."

"Let's not talk about that. Let's talk about how much we love you. I've never loved you more than I do now, Son."

"I love you too, Mom, but I don't deserve your love."

"A mother's love never dies." Mom went on to express her love in different ways. Leonard allowed his tears to flow freely.

Mom didn't ask personal questions. She must have wondered where he lived and what kind of a job he had, but she didn't ask. Leonard was grateful to be spared the embarrassment of trying to come up with an answer. For once, he didn't have a ready lie to save his face.

Leonard brought up family vacations. "Those were the best of times. When they were happening, I don't think I appreciated all the good things you did for me, but I do now." He started to name some of the memories that had been buried for a long time.

"We can have more good times together," Mom said wistfully. "When are you coming home, Leonard?"

Wanting to change the subject, Leonard fumbled for the right words. When a man waiting in line began to yell for the phone, Pastor Kurt tapped Leonard on the shoulder. The interruption came at an awkward moment in the conversation but Leonard was not ready to sign off. To the pastor, he said, "I've been gone a long time and this is the first time I've called. Mom and Dad thought I was dead. They still love me and want me to come home."

Pastor Kurt nodded approval.

"Please come home," Mom said.

"I wish I could, but I'm not ready."

"Of course you're ready. We'll come and get you."

"No, I wouldn't be any good for you. I uh - I wouldn't be able to leave the drugs alone."

"We'll get help. Whatever it takes, we want you back."

The offer sounded good but Leonard hesitated. "I don't know ..."

"Dad is standing here beside me and wants to talk to you."

Leonard feared that Dad might not be as forgiving as Mom was, but he said, "Come home, Son. We'll work it out." The tenderness in his father's voice touched Leonard's heart. He longed to go home more than anything else. Making a quick decision, he agreed to wait until his parents came to get him.

Walking over to stand by the truck, Leonard watched as other people made their calls. Tears. Smiles. Anguish. He noted a myriad of emotions. All the while he wondered what his future would bring. Could he get enough help to leave the drug world behind? What about finding a job? How could he face the people in town who had expected so much from him? Even as questions and doubts plagued his mind, he could hardly wait to see his parents again. Somehow he had to make good on the new beginning his parents offered him.

When the last person to make a call left, Pastor Kurt picked up the two chairs and headed for the back of the truck. He looked up to see Leonard and seemed startled. "What are you still doing here?" he asked.

"I called my parents and they're coming to get me?"

"When will they get here?"

"I don't know. They said it would take them about six hours. I've been waiting for quite a while."

Pastor Kurt unfolded the chairs and motioned for Leonard to sit down.

Although happy to have company, Leonard said, "You don't need to wait with me."

"The time will go faster if we sit together and talk," Pastor Kurt said.

Leonard liked to talk and lost no time in getting started. "Pastor Kurt, I'm curious about how you came to have the necklace in your truck. I once gave a birthday present like that to a friend."

"A young woman gave it to me yesterday. She said it was the most valuable thing she owned. It's supposed to remind me that I promised she could call her kids for free any time."

"Do you remember her name?"

"Yes. I know her well. It's Marlene."

Leonard gasped and closed his eyes. "Marlene! My friend from the motel. I can't believe it could be the same Marlene."

126

"Her mother runs a motel down near the Florida border."

Still amazed, Leonard said, "Mountain Breeze Motel. Wow! When I was young, my family used to stay there going to and coming from Florida. Dad always worked it out to stay there so he could avoid heavy traffic through Atlanta." He paused for a moment to reminisce, and then said, "That's my Marlene all right. Could you ... would you mind letting me hold the necklace?"

"Sure. I'll be glad to do that," the pastor said as he went to get the necklace.

Fingering the cross caused tears to well up in Leonard's eyes. "It's been so long. So many memories. How I wish I could be back there again. For sure, I would have made some better choices."

"It's never too late to start making good choices, Leonard."

Leonard shook his head. "Yeah, but it's just such a long way back there."

Pastor Kurt reached over to touch the cross. "The cross has great memories for me, too. It always humbles me to remember that Jesus died on that cross. I was a sinner but God loved me so much that He sent His only Son to pay the price for my sins and give me a new beginning." After a brief pause, the pastor added, "Jesus died to save you from your sins too, Leonard. If you decide to make that long trip back, you don't have to go it alone. Jesus will help you. He is the master of new beginnings."

"I'll keep that in mind." It would take some doing to convince Leonard that he could expect any help from Jesus, but he wanted to be open to all ideas. As he continued to examine the necklace, he asked, "Did you tell me that Marlene said this was the most valuable thing she owned?"

"Yes, those were her exact words."

"That's hard to believe it meant so much to her after all these years. I remember going shopping for this in Florida. I had saved quite a bit of money from mowing lawns and doing odd jobs. Always before, for Marlene's birthday, I had picked up a trinket from the beach, but I wanted to do something special for her fourteenth birthday. When I saw this in a jewelry store, I knew it was meant for Marlene. I liked it because it was unusual and unique. I guess that was what Marlene liked about it too." After a brief, thoughtful pause, he mused, "That was one of the few good things I have done in my life."

Nodding his head, Pastor Kurt said, "Anything we do to bring happiness to someone else brings even more happiness to ourselves."

Remembering the long line of people who made calls on the pastor's cell phone, Leonard said, "If that's true, you must be one happy man."

"I am one happy man," Pastor Kurt said.

For a few moments, as he stared at the necklace, Leonard's thoughts were too personal to share. Marlene's kiss. The way they had teased each other back and forth as he first stalled giving her the gift and then she delayed opening it. Finally, he had demanded, "Give me that bag. I want to put it on you." He could still sense the thrill of placing the necklace around Marlene's neck. For him, the kiss then sealed their love.

Best of all was Marlene's response that gave him a taste of royalty. She certainly played the part of a princess receiving the crown jewels. For one night in his life, he had felt like a prince, placed in the role by the girl he loved.

As time passed, Leonard said they had stopped writing and communicating. "I lived my life and she lived hers. We wouldn't know each other now."

Even with good conversation, time passed slowly. Pastor Kurt was a good listener as Leonard shared story after story about his experiences on the street – some true and some products of his active imagination. From time to time, Pastor Kurt offered an expression of sympathy or an encouraging word. Giving the necklace back to Pastor Kurt, Leonard smiled as he realized that Marlene valued their time together as much as he did.

After a few hours, Leonard expected his parents to arrive any moment. He could sit still no longer. Pacing around the chair, his heart beat faster and faster. Was fear or excitement the stronger emotion? he wondered.

Finally, a rusty Chevrolet drove slowly down the road. Recognizing his family members, Leonard stood up and began to yell and wave his arms. When the car stopped in the middle of the road, Leonard took off running. He reached the car just as Mom got out of the car, screamed in delight, took Leonard in her arms, and began to smother him with kisses. Even as his tears began to flow, Leonard realized that nothing had felt so right since he had left home. "I can't believe it, Mom. I can't believe we're together again," he said as the hugs and kisses started all over again.

"It's true and I don't want us to be separated ever again."

Dad stood nearby waiting patiently until Mom was ready to release her son. Greeting Dad was nearly as emotional for Leonard as it was to greet Mom. The two men were more successful in holding back the tears, but Leonard felt a very strong bond between them.

Before they got into the car to drive off, Leonard waved to Pastor Kurt, who seemed to genuinely enjoy watching the happy reunion take place.

"Jesus is the master of new beginnings!" Pastor Kurt mumbled. He smiled, got into his truck, and drove home.

Epilogue – Notes from Pastor Kurt

After two full days of sharing the intense emotions of the callers plus another four hours with Leonard, I was physically and emotionally exhausted. Every day I spend on the streets is full of encounters like those I experienced on that Mother's Day weekend, but the intensity of sharing one heartache after another and one moment of joy after another for extended periods of time put me on overload.

The anguish that Billy felt after learning of his mother's death continues to haunt me. No two words can pierce the human heart with pain more than "too late!" My hope and prayer for Billy is that he will reconcile with his heavenly Father before it is forever too late! Jesus beckons to him with open arms, but Billy must take the next step of accepting Jesus into his life.

When Erica put me on the phone with her father, I didn't know what to expect. He came right to the point. "We need your help, we want to come and get her – at least talk to her. Can you keep her there for a couple of hours until we can get there?"

Startled by the request and with no idea of how to carry it out, all I could say was, "I - I - I'll t-t-try."

"Please, please," he begged. "Keep her there because she won't stay. She always runs." He then asked to again speak with his daughter.

While he finished the conversation with Erica, I had only moments to come up with a plan. Lord, help me, I prayed and then said the first thing that popped into my mind. "I'm hungry." I felt foolish giving such detailed instructions and insisting that she go to a restaurant quite a distance away, but that was the only way I could think of - to buy time.

Also, I wanted to point her in the direction that had fewer drug dealers and opportunities to get into trouble. Time went slowly for her and for me. When her family finally showed up, I was overwhelmed with joy. She didn't run.

Witnessing the reunion with Erica and her parents brought me a moment of extreme joy. Watching the car drive away, though, my joy was mingled with sadness. I wished I could have introduced myself and shared in the reunion. Lord, You will have to take it from here, I prayed.

Mentally-challenged David presented me with an even greater dilemma. As soon as I got David's mother on the phone, she blurted out, "Wait! Don't give the phone to David yet. Please, please listen to me." I had no other option than to silently listen while trying to hold David off from grabbing the phone. "We've tried and tried to find David on the street, but he always outsmarted us. You have to help us," she pleaded.

"I will do what I can," I said.

"Above all, don't tell him anything. We can be there by noon tomorrow. I have your number on my caller ID. May I call you later tonight to get the directions?"

"Sure," I said as I wondered what I was getting myself into.

While David talked with his mother, I toyed with the idea of telling her that I couldn't give out directions unless she first talked to David and he agreed. The slim possibility that David would agree, though, caused me to hold off. David really needed to get off the streets. I have known David for years and a few times he almost lost his life from beatings and abuse. I knew he was "slow" and yet had enough smarts to stay ahead of most trouble. He had told me many times that he wanted to go home but was afraid. He had been lost for a long time and needed help, but I never tried to force him to do anything against his will.

Before hanging up the phone, David cried and told his mom he loved her. He apologized for being an embarrassment to the family and expressed his desire to change. The pathos in his voice convinced me that I had to help bring about a reunion between mother and son.

As David started to walk away, I came up with the idea of having him return the following day to wash my truck. Since the truck was dirty, that could be a good deal for both of us. The request seemed to confuse David and he didn't know how to respond. It was then that I came up with the idea of promising him a big reward. If the plan worked out, there would be a big reward for all of us.

133

That evening I was at home watching TV when David's mother Eleanor called. She was so glad to hear about the arrangement I had made with David. "Thank you, thank you so much," she said.

"I hope everything works out, but I have to tell you that I feel uneasy about my part in the plan. It's risky business to set someone up who is intentionally running from family no matter how noble of a thing it is to do."

"Please, please Pastor Kurt, you have to help us. David's father and I are getting older and we have tried so many times to find David. This may be our last chance." The desperation in Eleanor's voice was obvious and I wanted to help, but I needed to make one thing clear.

"If word gets out that I'm sneaking around trying to help families find their loved ones, I would be in a heap of trouble. In this case, I'm willing to go out on a limb for you, but I need you to promise that you won't try to force David to do anything he doesn't want to do. If he doesn't want anything to do with you, let him go. Is that a promise you can make to me?"

"Yes. All we want, Pastor Kurt, is to see David again. If he doesn't want to see us, we will leave. We love our boy and just want to let him know that we ..." Overcome by emotion, Eleanor could not go on.

David's father came on the line. "Mom is very worked up about this. Can you give us directions and we will meet you tomorrow?"

Between the two of us, we figured out the back roads that led from their town in Alabama to I-20 and the rest was easy. "I'm scared of driving in the big city and need clear directions of where to go when we get to Atlanta," he said. Once before, they had driven to Atlanta, where they thought they might find David. Driving the strange streets of the city had made both of them nervous wrecks.

Although I had Eleanor's promise that they would not do anything to force David to do anything he didn't want to do, I needed to hear it from his father too. With a chuckle, David's father said, "Pastor, we are old and couldn't force a fly into a bowl of soup." The humorist twist in the conversation put my mind at ease.

"Before we hang up, could I pray with you?" I asked. After a brief hesitation, he agreed. My heart overflowed with compassion as I asked God's guidance and direction in reuniting this family. When I finished, Eleanor got on the phone to again express her thanksgiving for my help. I hung up the phone hoping that, once again, "God would work good in all things."

The next question to concern me was, Would David show up on Sunday? By showing up early, though, he raised another question. Could I keep him busy until his parents arrived? I did a lot of stuttering as I continued to give instructions for more work to be done after he thought the job was finished. At any moment he might get disgusted and say, "I'm outta here."

All the while, of course, I wondered how David would react when his parents arrived. It could have been a traumatic experience for all of us. All I could do was pray that David and his parents would accept each other. David's burst of joy at the sight of his parents released all of my anxieties. Thank You, Lord, my heart repeated over and over again.

Thinking back now, I wonder, What were the odds of the vicarious connection between Marlene and Leonard through the necklace? I pray that tender memories of his childhood will go with Leonard back to Kentucky to help him begin a new life.

Long after Mother's Day Marlene continues calling her children and her mother. Whenever she sees me walking the streets, no matter the time, she calls home. Her mother always makes sure the girls take time to talk to their mother. Her mother knows that Marlene will probably never make it home and this may be the only connection their little ones will have with their mother - unless God works a miracle and Marlene is willing.

The necklace that continues to hang in my truck serves as tangible evidence that I serve a miracle-working God. Indeed, I could not even begin to do what I do in my own strength. But "I can do everything through him who gives me strength" (Phil. 4:13, NIV). I am blessed because, while working with the poor, I get to see God's miracles every day on Skid Row! Jesus is indeed the master of "new beginnings."